THIS BOOK BELONGS TO

Elizabeth A. Hoath.

14 South Bank

Westerham. Kent.

Oi Jimmy Knacker

The marble-players

Our corner of E13

1	Balaam Street	7	The Barrets	14	Harris's newsagent	21	The round seat
2	Dongola Road	8	The Gills	15	The Gibbses	22	The greenhouses
3	Khartoum Road	9	The Kimberleys	16	The Picture Palace	23	The tram sheds
4	Greengate Street	10	The Chamberses	17	The Greengate public house	24	Balaam Street School
5	'The top'	11	Old Ebbage	18	The YMCA	25	The fountain
6	Barber's Alley	12	The Mounts	19	The park	26	The sewer walk
		13	Dixon's corner shop	20	The bandstand		

Oi Jimmy Knacker

A memoir of an East Ender's childhood

—— *Ken Kimberley* ——

· MEMOIRS OF THE 20TH CENTURY ·
from
The NOSTALGIA *Collection*

For Joan and Bob,
and the Balaam Street boys
I was privileged to know

The soapbox derby

First published in October 1998

British Library Cataloguing in
Publication Data

A catalogue record for this book is
available from the British Library.

ISBN 1 85794 120 9

Silver Link Publishing Ltd
The Trundle
Ringstead Road
Great Addington
Kettering
Northamptonshire NN14 4BW

Printed and bound in Great Britain

Photographs by Brian Morrison

Contents

Oi Jimmy Knacker

'Oi Jimmy Knacker' was an East End street game of the 1930s, although in other parts of London it was known as 'Hi Jimmy Knacker'. In Croydon it was called 'Bury the Barrel', in Kirkcaldy it was 'Cuddy's Wecht', 'Mountikitty' on Tyneside, 'Bumberino' in South Wales and 'Pomperino' in Cornwall. In the Vnukour district of Moscow the game was known as 'Slona', and in Italy as 'Il cavallo lungo' ('the long horse'). A version of it is played in Turkey where it is known as 'Uzun Eshell' ('long donkey'), while in New York it is 'Johnny on the Pony'. It has even been seen in India and Japan.

Of all the street games this is the one that is readily remembered, possibly because it was the toughest, the one in which players were most frequently injured, and the one that required the greatest amount of stamina!

Two sides were chosen, and it was best to get the heftiest lads on your side. A boy known as the 'cushion' stood with his back to the lamp post, railings or whatever. The next in the team stooped down, placing his head in the cushion's stomach and holding on to his waist. The next boy in the team put his head under the second boy's legs and gripped his thighs, then the rest of the team did likewise. The 'horse' was then complete.

The other team was the 'jumping' team, who took it in turns to run across the street and jump on to the horse. Usually the best jumper in the team went first, for he had to endeavour to vault as far as he could along the horse, to enable the rest of his team to get on. Now all safely on the horse they sang a ditty, the E13 version of which was:

'Oi Jimmy Knacker, one, two, three,
One, two, three.
Oi Jimmy Knacker is got a flea,
Is got a flea.'

This was repeated three or four times. The team that won was the one that kept all its feet from touching the ground while perched on the horse's back during the singing of the ditty. For its efforts that team got another go.

A team also won if the horse collapsed under its weight. Of course, the 'jumping' team helped to bring this about by wriggling and bringing their combined weight to bear on the weaker part of the horse. If this happened, the riders all cried out 'Weak horses, weak horses, weak horses', then everyone chased across the street to the opposite pavement to start all over again.

Adapted from *Children's Games in Street and Playground* (Oxford University Press), © Iona and Peter Opie 1969

Introduction

'How are you today?' asked the Doctor.

'Fine, thanks,' I replied.

'Jolly good. We'll keep you here for a few more days, then it's off to Addenbrookes - they'll dig out anything I may have missed. Nothing to worry about, old chap. Addenbrookes across at Cambridge will sort you out!'

I put down Jeffrey Archer's latest novel and lay back on the pillow, looking up at the ceiling and thinking that I'd been jolly lucky over the years, this being my first ever stay in hospital! Hey, hold on a moment - that's not completely true. Was I six, maybe seven years old when they rushed me off to an isolation hospital in far-off Kent? 'Across the water' as Grandad would have it. Doctor Reid had said that I had diphtheria, or was it scarlet fever? I couldn't remember which.

I do remember coming home a few days later, cos old Doctor Reid had been mistaken, much to Mum's relief - it was nothing more than a mild dose of chicken-pox that all of us endured in our schooldays!

Grandad Thompson was furious cos he had been ordered out of house and home while it was fumigated, lock, stock and barrel, and, as Mum said in later years, 'My old Dad could be a bit "uppity" when he felt inclined to be.'

I smiled to myself, as I could imagine him to be just that. They said he was the last of the Victorians!

One memory led to another, and with little effort my early days at school came flooding back. Fond and not-so-fond memories of Old Murray, our teacher and his three Rs, and Old Tom Lethaby, the headmaster down at Balaam Street, came before me as if it was just yesterday! Grandad's favourite seat in the park, or sitting outside the Greengate pub at 'the top' with his cronies, the shiny red tram that took us off to Wanstead Flats for a penny, tiddler-fishing down at Becton. And how about all those street games - 'Knocking Down Ginger', 'Oi Jimmy Knacker', cricket against the lamp-post, when the ball inevitably ended up through some unfortunate's fanlight!

The early memories for me at that moment in time seemed endless. Was it the *Star of India* we waved our farewells to down at Custom House? Oh, what's in a name, I thought - it made little difference to the excitement Bob and I felt as we jumped out of our skins as the mighty siren blasted.

Did I remember rightly or wrongly if Ted Dale ever did score a hat-trick for Arsenal against Chelsea? It didn't matter as long as I remembered Grandad's jug full of wallop, and his classified *Star* on those long-ago Saturday nights.

I sat up in bed, thinking. I must transfer these memories to paper, so that they'll not be lost to me. A year or so before, although memories had been there they didn't have the same urgency as they did right now.

Of course there must be thousands like me with similar thoughts of yesteryear, the late 1920s, the '30s, early '40s, whether you lived in London, Liverpool or Leeds. We all enjoyed the same street games, got up to the same mischief, were chased out of the local park by 'old Parky', and looked up in awe and so much respect to the Mr Murrays of that world who taught us the three Rs.

Should I go and see for myself how my memories were looking these days? No, I thought, put it down on paper how you remember it - it'll be more fun that way!

A little later my wife Joan called in. 'Is there anything I can bring in tomorrow?' she asked.

'Oh, just a pad and pencil if you would.'

My walk down Memory Lane was under way!

About 50 sketches and five years, give or take a month or two, later, two old former school chums, Alfie and Ernie, and I decided to take the walk back to our roots. Brian Morrison took some photographs to compare with my 'memory sketches'. Of course there were differences between 'then' and 'now', brought about by the Blitz of the Second World War and the 60 or so intervening years, not to mention my memory.

Chas Mount, another old school pal in faraway Australia, got it so right when he wrote, 'Little else mattered in those happy carefree days, as long as we had a penny in our pockets to put into old Dixon's corner shop chewing-gum machine or to take us to Wanstead Flats for a day's adventure on that shiny red tram.'

Then Peter Townsend of Silver Link Publishing came across my sketches, saying, 'You know, Ken, you have here a little bit of social history. They're full of fun and of course a few tears. Let's make a book of them. . .'

Thanks, Peter!

First day

'But Grandad, I don't want to go to school!'

Granny Thompson

It was Saturday afternoon and they both carried their shopping bags because they had been up the road shopping. I could never remember them missing their Saturday afternoons out together.

'See you next week,' they would say, and Aunt Liz would hurry off down New Barn Street, Mum and me hurrying off down Balaam Street.

But today was different.

'Why are we going down here, Mum?' I asked.

'Sh, be quiet,' she said, as we walked down the dingy little side street. It was getting dark when Aunt Liz said, 'This is the house, Hadge.' Mum lifted the knocker and let it fall with a rat-a-tat.

The little room was almost as dark as the street outside. The gas mantle hissed and popped and barely gave enough light to reach us and the old lady as we stood around the table.

'How much is it our mum owes you?' I heard Mum ask her.

'Fifteen shillings,' she said.

Aunt Liz and Mum opened their purses. My eyes were level with the table top, as I watched my mum and my aunt carefully count out the silver coins and lay them on the table.

Outside in the dark street, Mum said, 'I'm glad that's over and done with, Liz.'

We hurried up to the bright lights of the top.

'Will you sort Dad's union money-box out, Hadge? Five shillings our mum said she borrowed from it!'

'Don't worry, Liz. I'll do it as soon as I get home. The trouble is our mum's got a heart of gold. She's too kind and caring for her own good. Anybody who knocks at the door, she always wants to help. But don't worry, I'll keep an eye on her in future.'

They said their goodbyes.

'See you next Saturday,' they promised each other.

Granny Thompson had two loving, caring daughters!

The old school where we learned the three Rs is no more! The site now boasts immaculate junior soccer and basketball facilities, all floodlit. Lucky young 'Hammers'!

'Come here, let me button up your coat. Oh, what a lovely satchel your mum has bought you. Turn around and let me have a look at you. Well, you do look smart,' she added, as once again she endeavoured to straighten my cap.

'But Gran, I don't want to go.'

'Don't be a silly boy. We all have to go to school,' she said. 'I remember taking your mum to school when she was a little girl, and all of your aunties and uncles. You'll learn how to read and write, do sums and make lots of new friends. Now, we don't want to be late, do we?'

She guided me up the passage to the street door. I looked forlornly back into the cosy kitchen, wondering if I would ever, ever see it again.

Shutting the door, Gran said, 'Miss Jenkins is ever so nice. Bobby liked her ever so much.'

'Where's Grandad?' I asked, as we crossed the street.

'Oh, he went off to get his *Daily Herald*. You'll see, he'll be waiting in the park for us.'

Mr Dixon was pulling his shop blind down.

'Well, well,' he said, 'and where are you off to in your Sunday best? And just look at the shine on your shoes!'

'I've got to go to school,' I mumbled.

Putting a big hand on my shoulder, Mr Dixon said, 'Sonny Jim, they'll be the best days of your life. Isn't that right, Gran?'

'That's what I keep telling him,' my Gran said.

''ere, 'alf a mo'.' He went back into his shop and when he reappeared he offered me a sherbet dab. I reached out for it and said,

'Thank you very much, Mr Dixon.' He and Gran exchanged a wink.

Hurrying along Balaam Street we entered the park, passing the fountain with its goldfish pond and bandstand.

'Look, there's Grandad.' He was sitting on his favourite seat, one which I often shared with him. I must have conveyed to Gran the urge I had to run across to him, because she closed her hand more firmly around mine. Grandad lifted his stick and waved.

'But Grandad,' I called, 'I don't want to go to school.'

Gran's hand tightened even more firmly around mine.

'Now, what's your name?' Miss Jenkins asked.

'Kenneth Kimberley,' I murmured.

'Well, Kenneth, we must find you lots of books and pencils to put in your satchel, and one day I'm sure that you will show me that you'll be as clever as your big brother!'

Delamura's ice-cream cart

'Please, Grandad, can I have a penny for an ice-cream cornet?'

'And don't be late back,' Miss Jenkins said as she opened the door and let us out of the classroom.

I crossed the school playground and took the short cut through the park and into Greengate Street, then hurried along to the Greengate.

In the summer it was one of Grandad's favourite resting places, as he called them. It was here, seated on the wooden benches, that he and his friends put the world to rights, so Gran would say – whatever that meant!

There he was. So, too, was old Delamura's ice-cream cart, with its red and white striped top.

'Hello Grandad,' I said, adding, 'Please can I have a penny for an ice-cream cornet?'

'He knows where to find you when he wants an ice-cream,' said Ted, the bookie's runner.

'There you are, lad,' Grandad would always say, taking a penny from his waistcoat pocket, adding as he did so, 'Don't tell your Gran that you've seen me sitting here, will you, there's a good boy.'

'Thank you, Grandad – I won't tell Gran.'

Delamura dipped into his tub and gave me the biggest ice-cream cornet you ever saw. A few minutes later I stepped over Gran's freshly whitened doorstep and called, 'It's me Gran. I'm home from school.'

'About time, too,' she mumbled to herself as she hurried up the passage and opened the door. 'Have you seen your Grandad?' she asked.

'Well, er, hmm. . .' I hated telling

fibs to Gran, but I had promised Grandad. Thankfully she answered for me.

Grandad and his pals wouldn't recognise the Greengate pub today because it's been completely rebuilt. I doubt if old Delamura with his ice-cream cart would either. Note today's version by the traffic lights.

'I know,' she said. 'He's sitting outside the Greengate with that Ted. I know cos there's ice-cream all down your shirt front. Just you wait till he comes home.'

I hurried down the passage into the kitchen.

'Gran, what's for dinner?' I asked. 'And Miss Jenkins said we mustn't be late back to school.'

Ted Alder

'Mum, Mr Alder is always stood outside the phone box up at the top. What does he do, Mum?'

Hesitantly she said, 'He's a bookie's runner.'

'What's that?' I asked.

She looked about her and hummed and ha'ed. 'Don't you ever tell anybody, will you, cos 'e's breaking the law really, cos he takes bets from people to put on horses they fancy might win at the races.'

'Do you mean he might have to go to prison?' I asked.

'Well, I don't know about that,' she replied with a smile. 'They've got to catch old Ted first with a betting slip.' Tapping her forehead, she continued, 'He keeps it all up here. He has a marvellous memory. No, old Ebbage'll never catch 'im at it, mark my words!'

'But I've seen 'im, Grandad and Sergeant Ebbage sitting together outside the Greengate. They must all be friends,' I said.

'Oh yes,' she said. 'They're old sparring partners.'

'What's a sparring partner?' I asked.

'Oh come on, Ken, I haven't the time to stand about talking all day!'

Sunday morning

'When will I be old enough to be a cub, Grandad?'

'Your bag of washing gets heavier every Sunday,' and with a twinkle in his eye Grandad added, 'I'll ask Harry Ponder if I can borrow his vegetable barrow.'

'Oh Dad, get along with you. What will the neighbours think?'

Grandad turned to me and said, 'Come on, Sonny Jim, let's get out of your mother's way and catch a tram up at the top.'

'Here it comes. Oh, it's an open top. Can we go upstairs?' I asked.

'All right then,' and much to Grandad's relief the conductor said, 'You can put the bag under the stairs, guv.'

I climbed the stairs and hurried along to the front seats. Huffing and puffing, Grandad followed behind. Everything looked different up here. I could reach out and touch the leaves as the branches arched over the street below. I could see old Harris watering his flowers in the yard behind his shop. Next door Mrs Ponder was sitting at her bedroom window. In the yard below, Mr Ponder was washing down his barrow.

A tram dashed past us going the other way. I jumped back in fright. Grandad held on to his straw hat, with hair ruffled and eyes watering.

'Wasn't it going fast, Grandad?'

'Fares please, fares please!'

'One and a half to Becton Road, conductor,' and at that moment we heard the band:

'Onward, Christian soldiers,
Marching as to war,
With the cross of Jesus,
Going on before.'

Grandad was humming away and tapping his stick on the floor in time with the advancing music, with bugles blaring, drums beating and banners held high. The policeman held up the traffic with his large, white-gloved hands as the long column of Scouts and Cubs, with backs straight and arms swinging, passed below us.

'When will I be old enough to be a Cub, Grandad?'

'When your Sunday school card is full of red stars,' he replied. 'Come on lad,' he added, still tapping his stick to the now fading Christian soldiers. 'We have to get off at the next stop.'

Aunt Liz was standing at her gate. 'Uncle Bill and Billy are in the yard,' she said.

I hurried up the passage, through the kitchen, down the step into the scullery, and out into the yard.

'Your Aunt Liz loves her flowers,' I often heard Mum say. There were all sorts and colours everywhere, running along and up over the fence and climbing over Uncle Bill's chicken run. A tree in the corner, as high as the bedroom window, was covered in tiny white stars. Bending low, Uncle Bill stepped out of the chicken run. Billy followed, his hands holding his jersey taut in front of him – it was full of brown, speckled newly laid eggs. Aunt Liz brought a bowl from the kitchen and carefully filled it.

'There you are,' she said. 'They'll do nicely for your breakfasts next week.' Taking some scissors from her pinafore, she added, 'I'll just cut some flowers for your mum.'

Uncle Bill came from the kitchen with a glass of beer for Grandad and himself, and a glass of lemonade for Billy and me. We made ourselves comfortable on the kitchen window-sill and the grown-ups talked while we sat and listened.

Emptying his glass, Grandad said, 'Come on, lad, time we were off cos dinner will be ready.'

The Abbey Arms pub remains unaltered from when it was built in 1882, with the local newsboy's stand still outside. The public conveniences also remain, but the old blacksmith's around the corner has gone. Almost next door, Hitchcock's the undertakers still tends to the deceased as it did in my grandfather's day.

Uncle Bill popped his weekly Sunday penny into my hand, saying with a smile, 'Don't forget. Once you're 14 and off out to work there'll be no more Sunday pennies.'

We said our goodbyes at the gate. Grandad picked up the bag of newly washed clothes. In one hand I carried Mum's flowers, while tightly clenched in the other was the bowl of eggs.

Sitting on the tram as it made its way down Balaam Street, I asked, 'Grandad, if I'm six now, how many Sunday pennies will I have saved by the time I'm 14?'

'Oh,' he said, 'you'd better ask the brains of the family that one.'

'Grandad, why does Aunt Liz do our washing?'

'Cos your mum goes to work all the week and doesn't have the time to,' he replied.

'She's very kind. I like Aunt Liz. She's my favourite aunt,' I said.

Mum opened the door. I gave her the flowers and eggs, and dashed up the passage.

'Bob! Bobby! If I'm six now, how many Sunday pennies will I have saved by the time I'm 14?'

The swing-bridge

'Look, Grandad, those men up there have all got black faces!'

When we arrived home from school, Grandad said, 'There's a boat leaving the docks. Let's go and see her off.' The toast, cakes and tea were quickly scoffed and Children's Hour was forgotten as we made our way to Custom House.

Soon our noses were pressed firmly against the iron gates; waiting with us, but not so excited, were the lorry drivers, giving the impression that they were not enjoying the long wait as we were.

'Here she comes,' Grandad announced.

'Gosh, isn't she big? She's as long as Balaam Street,' said Bob.

'Where's she going? Will it take long to get there?' we asked, cos Grandad knew everything!

It was early evening. Lights twinkled from a hundred places up above us. Men waved down to us, we waved back.

'Look Grandad, they've all got black faces,' I said.

There was so much to see as the *Star of India* went slowly by. Two long blasts on her siren had us jumping out of our skins.

'She's out in the river now,' said Grandad.

With this the lorry drivers started their engines and edged towards the iron gates, satisfied looks on their faces, disappointment on ours. We watched as the swing-bridge moved. The man in the peaked cap came from his hut, raised his arm, and as if by magic the iron gates rolled aside.

'All right, Charlie,' he said to Grandad, and to us, 'What did you think of her, lads?'

'Cor!' was all we could find to say.

The buses and lorries hurried by, anxious to be on their way home.

'Come on boys, your mother will be home from work with the supper on. We'd better not be late.'

After supper, when the kitchen table was cleared, Grandad opened our atlas. Durban would be the first port of call, then across the Indian Ocean to Bombay.

'What will it be like there, Grandad? Do they have to go to school like us? Do they play football and cricket?'

Grandad placed his finger on each far-off place as he traced the *Star of India*'s voyage across the world for us to see.

'Oh, we do wish we could go! If we do, will you come with us Grandad?'

Sleeping soundly that night, we could not have dreamed that in a few short years our wishes would be granted. Sadly, Grandad wouldn't be coming with us.

Grandad Thompson

Grandad Charlie Thopmpson was born in Deal, Kent, in 1863. He became a tinsmith and followed the fishing boats along the South Coast and up to South Wales, plying his trade making tins for the fishermen's catches. He came to London and married Liza Flight, my Gran, who was born in Limehouse.

The Thompson family Bible records that Aunt Annie was their first-born in 1885 and died soon after. Aunt Gert was born in 1887, Uncle Charlie in 1888, Alfred in 1891; he too died in his boyhood days. Uncle George came along in 1893, Aunt Liz in 1894, our mum, Harriet, in 1896, Uncle Tom in 1899, Aunt Florence in 1902 – she died in her teens – and Uncle Jim in 1904!

In the early 1900s the Thompsons moved from Poplar to Plaistow E13 and the family's long association with the school in the park down Balaam Street began. At one time or other from the early 1900s Charlie Thompson's children and grandchildren made their way along Balaam Street through the park and into school.

My brother Bob and I loved Grandad; for us he was our Dad and Grandad all rolled into one!

Saturday night

'Hello, young man, jugful of the usual wallop is it?'

Taking the jug from the dresser, Grandad said, ''ere's a shilling. Be a good lad and pop up the top and get it filled for me, and don't forget my *Star*, will you?'

It was Saturday night, and I always ran this errand for him, knowing of course that when I arrived back I would get my customary penny.

'Hello, young man. Jugful of the usual wallop, is it?'

'Yes please,' I replied.

'There's an Old Mill by the Stream' filled my ears as the regulars accompanied the piano in the saloon bar next to the jug & bottle.

When I stepped out on to the pavement the newsboy was calling,

'Read all about it! Ted Drake gets a hat trick for the Gunners!'

Wally Chambers was buying his *Star*. Seeing me, he said,

'Hello young Kenny. I see you've got your Grandad's favourite tipple there.'

The Chambers family lived next door to us. He hurried away as Harry Ponder went across the traffic lights, pushing his empty barrow on his way home.

'Standing room only in the sixpennies and ninepennies!' I could hear the man in the red coat, peaked cap and white gloves calling out as he carefully counted and ushered the lucky few through the door of the picture palace opposite. The long queue shuffled patiently

forwards as the barrel-organ kept them company.

'*War Cry* – only a penny!' The Salvation Army lady opened the door of the saloon bar and did her utmost to compete with 'Nellie Dean' and the piano. I left them all to it – the bright lights, the noise and the bustle of the top – and hurried home, carefully clutching Grandad's jug in one hand and his *Star* in the other.

Grandad took the red-hot poker from the grate and plunged it into the jug of stout, saying, 'There you are, lad, that'll put a bit of life into it.' It frothed up and ran all over the hearth.

'Cor!' I thought. 'Good job Gran's not here to see that!'

'That'll put a bit of life into it,' he said.

The funeral

'Mr Hitchcock has come to take Grandad away,' said Bob.

'Please can I put the wireless on? It's Children's Hour.'

'No, not today,' replied Mum. 'You must both be very quiet.

Grandad's very ill in bed upstairs.'

We knew something was wrong cos Mum hadn't been to work for two days.

Aunt Liz

'Here she comes, Gran. Here comes Aunt Liz.'

I was standing at the window watching out for her while Gran had her customary forty winks upstairs in the front bedroom.

'Go and open the door for her then,' said Gran, 'and be careful how you go downstairs.'

I hurried down the stairs, up the passage and opened the door. Aunt Liz came in with her big black shopping bag that almost touched the ground.

'Gran's having her forty winks,' I said.

'Oh all right, I'll put the kettle on then.'

In those very early days I saw more of our Aunt Liz than my mum, cos Mum was off to work before I was awake, and I was in bed before she arrived home. Bob, who was older than me, was allowed to stay up later, so he saw her more than I did!

When Gran died we saw even more of Aunt Liz. She came round to our house at dinner time and tea time. Billy, my cousin, would come with her.

On winter evenings we would sit in front of the kitchen stove with our toasting forks. Making sure we had filled ourselves up with hot buttered toast, Aunt Liz would say, 'Come on, Billy, we'd better be getting off home

cos your Dad will be home from work soon.' Then to Bob and me, 'Now, you'll be all right till your mum gets home. Don't let the fire go out, will you, Bobby?' Then off home she would go.

This went on until it was thought that I was old enough to go to Aunt Liz's at meal times. Leaving the school in Balaam Street, I would run all the way to the house in Chadwin Road. After dinner Aunt Liz would go to her pantry under the stairs.

'Here you are, Kenny,' she would say as she opened the biscuit barrel. 'I know you like coconut biscuits.'

'Oh thanks, Aunt Liz. See you tomorrow.'

She would wave to me from her gate as I dashed off back to school.

Bob caught pneumonia in his early days in the RAF, and at one time there were doubts whether he would pull through. Mum received a letter from him from Scotland where he was in hospital. It said in the feeblest of writing that the two people he wished to see more than anything else were our Mum and his Aunt Liz! That surely summed up the feelings we both had over the years for kind, caring Aunt Liz.

She lived on to the grand age of 94, never wishing to move from her beloved Plaistow!

Aunt Liz came into the kitchen with the coal-scuttle. 'The fire's getting low in Dad's bedroom. I'll get some more coal in.'

'I'll get it,' Bob said. Aunt Liz turned to Mum and I heard her say, 'I don't think Dad will last the night.'

There was a knock on the street door. It was Uncle Jim.

'Hello young Kenny,' he said. 'What have you been up to today?'

Uncle Tom followed behind. I closed the door and watched as they made their way upstairs. They joined Uncle Bill and Uncle Charlie who had come earlier. We could hear Aunt Liz making up the fire.

Later Mum came down into the kitchen. 'Your Grandad wants to see you both.'

We tiptoed up the stairs. Uncle Jim was drawing the curtains. The fire came to life and lit up the room. I watched the flames

flickering and reflecting in the brass rails behind Grandad's pillows. Mum led me down one side of the large bed and Bob went down the other side. Grandad reached out to Bob and I heard him say, 'Look after your Mum, won't you?' Then to me he said, 'Be a good lad and do as your mum tells you.'

Aunt Liz guided us both

downstairs. Moments later Mum hurried down. 'Dad's gone, Liz.'

Bob peeped through the blinds and said, 'Look, Mr Hitchcock has come to take Grandad away.'

I looked back into the parlour. The round table with its long cloth that reached to the floor had been pushed into the corner, and two wooden trestles occupied the centre of the room. We had lost count of the number of times we had opened the street door for all the aunts and uncles, neighbours and friends who had come to see Grandad for the last time. I carefully brushed aside some flower petals and leaves that lay scattered on the oilcloth.

'Bob,' I whispered, 'it smells like the flower shop in Balaam Street.'

Uncle George looked down at us from above the mantelpiece. He had gone to France in the Great War and had never come back. I turned back to the blinds and peeped out with Bob. Everything was shining and black, just as Grandad's boots had always been.

The family followed Mr Hitchcock out through the gate. Uncle Jim was the last to leave. As he did so he caught my eye and gave me a small smile. I turned away and looked at the round table with its long velvet cloth, wondering if we would ever play hide and seek under it again.

The school outing

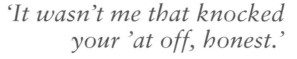

'It wasn't me that knocked your 'at off, honest.'

I picked up the letter off the doormat. It was addressed to Mum. Across the top was printed 'County Borough of West Ham Education Department'.

'Gee whiz, I bet it's my school scholarship examination result.'

I laid it on the kitchen table for her for when she came home that evening.

Today was my last day at Ravenhill Junior Boys School in Cave Road. The summer holidays started tomorrow, at the end of which my school pals and I, depending on the news that was dropping on the doormats at that very moment, would be going our separate ways. However, scholarships and exams were forgotten on this sunny summer's day as I hurried across Greengate Street on my way to school. Turning the corner I saw the three Playfair open-top buses that were waiting

outside the school to take us on the outing. I joined the rest, all excited, as we lined up to get a seat.

'Cor, 'ope I get a seat on the top!' was the main cry.

The teachers ushered us on to a bus, and with much noise and excitement we scrambled to find a seat.

'It wasn't me that knocked your hat off, sir. Honest, sir, it wasn't me!'

Mr Thurston grabbed at and managed to hold on to his trilby before it sailed over the side of the bus.

'Honestly, sir, it wasn't me,' continued the guilty boy, still declaring his innocence above the noise and lots of waving to the onlookers on the pavement below. Ding, ding, ding, ding went the bell and we were on our way.

At regular intervals Mr Thurston called out, 'You boys up the front – do sit down in your seats!'

This is where we lined up, all excited to get on the Playfair buses. Part of our junior school still stands, but the former playground and main school building have been demolished; in their place is an African Caribbean Elders Day Centre.

'Where are we, Mr Thurston?' somebody asked. 'Is it lousy Loughton?'

'Steady on, steady on!' he shouted. 'You'll break your necks!'

We ignored his advice in our rush to be first off the bus.

An old man slowly opened the gate, and sensibly stood aside as a small army of East End schoolboys swooped into the deserted green meadow. We tumbled and rolled around, and chased each other in the soft, yielding grass, which not a bit like the cold, hard asphalt in the school playground. The shrill blast of a whistle brought our rough and tumble to an end.

'Right boys,' Mr Kingston called. 'Sort yourselves into four groups.'

After much hustle and bustle we did this, then each teacher led his group into a far corner of the field. Footballs, cricket bats and stumps, and rounders bats were quickly produced. Each group by now had divided itself into teams, and the rest of the day was devoted to our favourite games. From time to time at a blast from old Kingston's whistle we all changed corners, playing rounders one minute and cricket the next. Relay and 100-yard races were won and lost. At the end of it all, when legs began to wobble and enthusiasm began to wane, one more long blast on the whistle brought the games to a close.

The teachers rounded us up. 'Come on, lads, it's teatime.'

We followed them into the big white tent. After the heat and excitement of the day it was airy and cool inside. A long wooden table stretched down the middle with bench seats on either side. At intervals in the middle of the table were trays of buns and sandwiches, rosy red apples and juicy looking pears. Two ladies were busy filling large teapots from the urns that stood on the table.

'Sit down, lads,' the teachers called out, and with a scramble we

did as they asked, as the ladies came down the long table filling our mugs.

'Help yourself, boys!' We needed no second telling. 'Eat as much as you wish, but don't waste any!'

There was little time for talking as we set about the trays and scoffed as much as we wanted.

On the way home we sat quiet and tired after the excitement of the long day.

'Where have we been to, Mr Thurston?' we asked.

'Oh, Ockenden, North Ockenden.'

The bus became quieter and quieter, and in next to no time we began to recognise the old familiar streets. We tumbled down the stairs and out on to the pavement by the school, then all drifted away. As we did I heard Whiteley's sweet factory's hooter sounding.

'It must be 5 o'clock,' I thought.

Jimmy Neaster and I walked up Dongola Road together. He turned and said, 'My Dad had a letter from the school board this morning. My Mum said it's probably the result of the scholarship examination. I wonder what's inside it.'

Like me, I thought, he would have to wait until later when his Dad, like my Mum, came home from work. He left me at the corner and went off to his home above the toy shop in Balaam Street.

I felt for the front door key in my trouser pocket, relieved that it was still there after all the running and

chasing about during the day. Picking up the letter again, I put it by the clock on the mantelpiece, then laid the kitchen table for supper.

Sitting in Grandad's old chair by the fireplace, I turned the pages of last week's *Magnet* and laughed aloud at the antics of Billy Bunter, Harry Wharton, and Co. The day at North Ockenden, the Playfair buses and the letter on the mantelpiece were temporarily forgotten.

Summer holidays

It was the first day of our summer holidays, and we were waiting for the tram in Balaam Street, armed to the teeth with fishing-nets, tent-poles, lemonade powder and bottles of water to make fizzy lemonade to quench our thirsts during the long summer day. Across the street Mrs King was pointing up to her chimney-pot.

'Well I can't see it,' she was saying to old Blackie, the sweep.

'Well I can,' he replied.

'So can we,' we all joined in, and pointed to where old Blackie's brush could be seen against the blue summer sky. As Gran used to say, you never paid Blackie until you could see his brush out of the chimney-pot. Just like the coalman. You must count every bag as he carried them down the passage. Seemed that old Mrs King thought as Gran did.

Blackie and Mrs King were quickly forgotten as the eagerly awaited, shiny red tram came swaying down Balaam Street and stopped before us.

'Oi, I hope you've all got your fares,' the conductor said to us.

'Course we have!' and we quickly climbed the stairs to the outside.

'And no larkin' about up there, mind,' he called after us.

''ere, mister, wait for Podgy,' someone called as, last as always, Podgy scrambled up on to the platform, reached on tiptoe and pulled the bell cord. Ding, ding, ding, ding went the bell, and we were off.

Old Tom Lethaby, Mr Murray, Old Solly, Mr Cohn and Balaam Street School were quickly forgotten as we set off on our first adventure of the holidays, which stretched before us for weeks and weeks – our very own trees to climb in our very own forest, with ponds full of tadpoles and tiddlers. Each passing day would be an adventure, just like Tarzan at the pictures.

Old Blackie

I helped Mum spread the newspapers over the oilcloth in the parlour. The piano, her pride and joy, was carefully covered together with everything else with an assortment of sheets. Gran's clock was taken from beneath its glass dome on the mantelpiece, and Uncle George was taken down.

'Look how the wallpaper's faded,' she said. 'Don't believe it's been done up since your Uncle Jim got married to your Aunt Edie. Fetch me some more newspapers. They're on the copper in the scullery.'

I helped her spread them up the passage to the street door. 'That'll do,' she said. 'Old Blackie said we would be his first call.'

'Well,' said Blackie when he arrived, 'you've grown up. I 'aven't seen you since your old Gran was alive.' He walked down the passage and into the parlour, carrying his brushes and sacks. He smelled all sooty.

Later he poked his head around the kitchen door. 'Where's the missus, lad?'

Mum was busy lighting the copper in the scullery.

'Thought you'd want to see me brush out of the top of the pot,' and through his soot-lined face his eyes twinkled as he said, 'just like yer old mum, cos she wouldn't pay me till she saw me brush out of her chimney-pot!'

We followed him across the street. He pointed up to the roof-top and proudly said, 'There she is then.'

'Go and fetch my purse, Ken. It's on the mantelpiece in the kitchen.'

Between us we picked up the last newspaper.

'Now I'll pop these sheets in the copper. The water will be lovely and hot now.'

Standing at the parlour door, she looked longingly at the faded wallpaper patch over the fireplace. 'Think I'll ask your Uncle Bill if he'll do the parlour up for me,' she said.

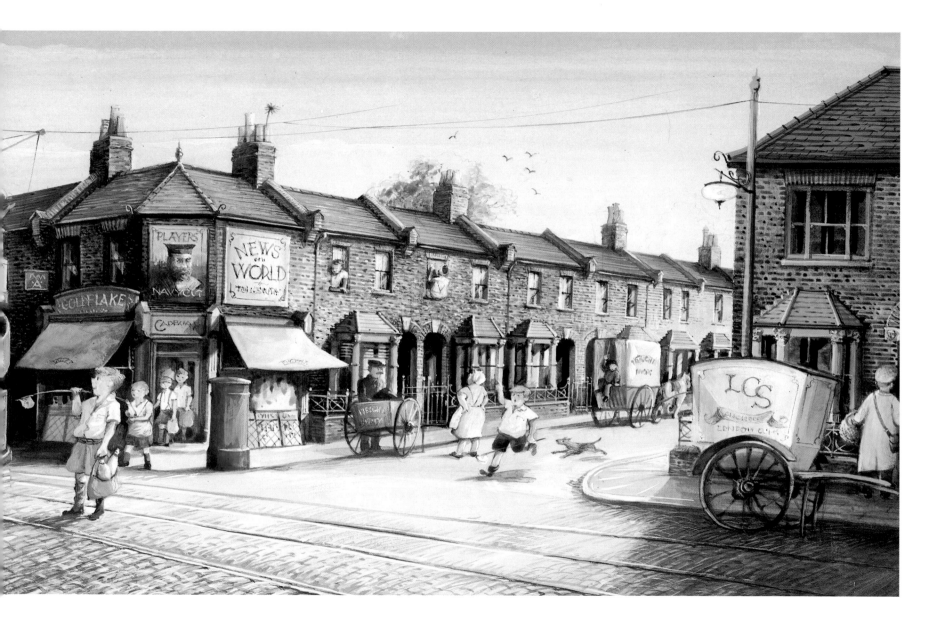

Sunday best

It all looked gloomy and spooky, so I kept close to Mum and Bob.

It was Sunday best day. We stood in front of Mum in our grey flannel suits, collars, ties and shiny shoes. Nodding her approval with a 'You'll do', we went off the church. A star was stamped on our cards to prove that we had been, as it was so very tempting to go elsewhere.

'Lay the table please,' Mum asked us when we arrived back home.

Bob laid out the plates while I found the knives and forks in the dresser. There to one side were our aprons. Oh, I did wish Mum wouldn't ask us to put these on over our Sunday best.

Coming from the scullery, she said, 'Put your aprons on then.'

'But Mum. . .' we both exclaimed.

Her look was enough, and we did as she asked.

'Oh well, it's best that we get gravy stains on our aprons rather than on our best suits,' said Bob.

'That's all right, so long as they don't see me like this at school,' I thought.

Later, Mum came downstairs saying, 'Are you both ready? Put your raincoats on in case it rains.'

We walked up to the top and waited for a No 40 bus. When it arrived, we asked, 'Can we go upstairs?'

'Oh all right, if you must.'

We ran the length of the bus and sat in the front seats. We got off at the end of Green Street and walked the rest of the way to Woodgrange Park Cemetery, stopping as usual at the gates where Mum bought her flowers.

'Carry these for me please, Bob,' Mum said, handing him a bunch of flowers while she carried the others. He didn't like doing this at all. Once, out of Mum's hearing, he said to me that he felt a sissy carrying flowers.

We walked up the gravel drive. If it was a nice sunny day I would scamper off ahead, picking my way among the gravestones until I found Dad's, but today it was dull and miserable and on these occasions everywhere looked gloomy and spooky, so I kept close to Bob and Mum.

Mum put her carrier bag on the grass and with a damp cloth carefully cleaned the marble headstone. Bob and I picked out the odd blade of grass that had dared to show itself among the marble chips.

Mum took the fading flowers from the urn and handed them to Bob. We knew that our next job would be to get the fresh water and put the old flowers on the waste tip. We went off and left her alone, always speaking in whispers, and carried fresh water in a watering-can back to the graveside. Mum carefully arranged the fresh flowers, had a last look round as if to approve of our efforts, then we went off to find Gran and Grandad.

Walking back down the gravel drive to the cemetery gate, Mum said, 'Oh, look at your shoes, Ken. I don't know how you get them in such a state.' She offered Bob the damp cloth from her bag. As he bent down and cleaned them for me, he said, still whispering, 'You're old enough to clean your own shoes now.'

It started to drizzle with rain.

'Well,' Mum said, 'I don't think we will go for a bus ride this afternoon. Never mind, perhaps it will be a nicer day next Sunday.'

The bus ride

'And how many are you going to buy today, Sonny Jim?'

'Can we go on top?' came the familiar cry.

'Well you always do,' Mum said with a smile.

The front seats were empty as we hurried along the top deck and sat down. Paddy sat under Bob's seat, and Mum sat on the seat behind us.

On this particular Sunday afternoon, as we left the cemetery Mum had said, 'As it's a fine afternoon let's go for a bus ride.'

We knew that she enjoyed the ride as much as we did, because she enjoyed looking at the new houses that were being built near the end of the bus ride.

'Fares, please! Fares, please!'

'One and two halves to Chadwell Heath, please.'

'Can I have the tickets, please, Mum?' I asked. She handed me one long blue one and two short pink ones, and I put them safely in my pocket. After a while open fields took the place of houses and shops. There were no tram-lines and no lamp-posts, and the roadway was smooth and not like the cobblestones down Balaam Street.

'All change for Sunshine Homes!' called the conductor from downstairs.

'Come on,' said Mum. 'This is where we get off.'

As I stepped down from the platform, the conductor said, 'And how many are you going to buy today, Sonny Jim?'

He pulled the bell cord and gave us a wave as the bus drove off. We stood on the grass verge and looked up at the big sign opposite: 'Sunshine Homes for sale. £450. Enquiries. . .'

'I won't be a moment,' Mum said as she walked up the path to the green-painted shed. Minutes later she reappeared. 'I've got the key to the house that's finished.'

We stood on the step as she opened the street door. The newness of it all – the smell of paint and freshly distempered walls and snow-white ceilings – took our breath away. Mum led the way down the passage. Clump, clump, clump went our shoes on the bare boards. We passed the staircase with its glossy painted banister rails and went into the kitchen. We knew that this was our Mum's dream as she ran her hand over the deep white sink, with its two chromium-plated taps.

'Gee, Mum,' said Bob. 'It says hot and cold.'

'Yes,' she said. 'It's what's called a butler's sink.'

All round the sink and up to the window ledge were glistening white tiles. She turned and opened the glass-paned door of the big dresser, closed it, then opened the drawers beneath. We looked out of the window above the sink. The long narrow garden seemed to go on for ever.

'Can we go upstairs?' we asked.

'Yes, I'll be up in a moment.'

We left her to it in the kitchen and went up the stairs two at a time. It was all light and airy up there. Light seemed to flood into the rooms from every direction.

'Gee whiz, come and look in here!' Bob called out. 'I'm in the bathroom. I've never been in a real bathroom before.'

We looked at the gleaming white bath. Next to it, under the window, was a basin that had the same chromium taps as those on the bath.

On the other wall was a lavatory with a shiny, lift-up seat. It wasn't a bit like ours at home, where you had to go out into the yard if you wanted to use it!

As we went downstairs, Mum came up. I said, 'We've already found the best room for our railway, haven't we, Bob?'

With a last longing look into the kitchen, Mum said, 'Come on boys. We must return the key now.'

As she closed the street door the man from the green-painted shed

came up the path and raised his trilby hat.

'Well,' he said to Mum, 'is it what you're looking for?' To us he said, 'Lots of room in the garden for cricket and football, lads.'

'Yes,' I said, 'and I know where I'm going to have our railway.'

Mum and the man walked slowly along the pavement together, talking as they did so. They stopped outside the green shed. Mum handed him the key, and he lifted his hat.

'Goodbye Mrs Kimberley. Nice to have met you and your two boys.' To us he added, 'Now lads, keep saving up all your pocket money and come and live in the countryside.'

'Thank you and goodbye, Mr Young,' said Mum.

'Well,' said the conductor, 'it's you again. Did you buy up the street then?'

On the way home I heard Mum say to Bobby, 'I can't afford it yet, and it's a long way to go to work at Hackney, and you're doing very well at the secondary school. You wouldn't wish to move, would you?'

Paddy made himself more comfortable under the seat as Bobby replied, 'I'll be going to work one day and I'll be able to help.'

'It's a long time yet,' Mum said with a smile. 'We'll just have to wait and see.'

The excursion

We were soon all lost in a cloud of steam.

'Ken, see who is at the street door.'

I put the *Wizard* down and hurried up the passage. 'Hello Kenny. Is your mum home yet?'

'Mum,' I called, 'it's Mrs Gill.'

'Well, ask her in then.'

Mrs Gill went down the passage into the kitchen. Mum and her had been friends for a long time; they had grown up and been to school together.

'I can see you're busy getting the supper on,' said Mrs Gill, 'so I won't keep you a minute. We're having a day at Southend tomorrow cos there's an excursion on. It's only a shilling return, and I wondered if your two boys would like to come along with us.'

'That's very kind of you, Lilly,' Mum said. 'You'd like that, wouldn't you, Ken?'

'Oh yes!' I said. 'Bobby's in the parlour doing his homework, but I'm sure he would wish to go too.'

'Well I'll give them a knock at nine then.'

'There you are, Lilly. Here's two shillings for their fares. I'll give them a bit of pocket money in the morning.'

They stood together at the street door chatting for a while, then Mum came back into the kitchen saying, 'Well, that was kind of Mrs Gill to think of you both. I'll have to get your Sunday best out!'

I went upstairs to the boxroom. Along one side we had made a narrow trestle table to lay out our Hornby train set, carefully adding to it when our pocket money permitted. It was our pride and joy. It had a station, with porters and passengers waiting for the train. We had signal-boxes and signals, bridges and tunnels. On the wall behind Bob had painted fields and distant hills, and a blue sky that reached almost to the ceiling. A horse and cart made its way along a country lane. It all looked ever so real. But tomorrow, thanks to Mrs Gill, we would be sitting on and looking at the real thing!

'Here it comes!' We strained our necks and stood on tiptoe as the Southend excursion came into view. Anxious parents held on to small hands.

'Stand back! Stand back!' called the porter, and with a big sigh, a grunt and a groan the shiny black engine stopped in front of us, and we were all soon lost in a cloud of steam. There was much excitement

as doors opened and closed with a clatter along the platform, and Mums and dads guided their Alfies, Billies and Bets into the nearest compartment.

'This one will do us, Charlie,' called out Mrs Gill.

I remember steam and smoke, but not the weeds. I bet you can't get to Southend and back for a shilling – 5p – today!

'Are there any corner seats?' he asked.

'Oh, what does it matter as long as we have a seat?' she replied, adding anxiously, 'Where are the boys?'

We were watching the engine-driver lean on the side of his cab, lift his cap and wipe his forehead and hands with his oily cloth. He looked down at us.

'Oi, mister,' called out Eddy. 'What's it like up there?'

'Ruddy hot on a summer's day like this – but mind you, if you're an engine-driver like me you can go to the seaside every day of the week!'

'Come on, you boys,' shouted an irate and anxious Mr Gill, 'or you'll miss the train.'

The guard put his whistle to his lips and unfurled his green flag as we scampered off down to the last open door and fell into the carriage. A red-faced Mr Gill slammed it shut. With more clouds of steam, puffs of smoke, and jerks and jolts we were off to Southend-on-Sea!

On the pier

'Oh, I'm fed up with making sand-castles for all of you,' said Bob. 'I'm going for a walk on the pier.'

'I'll come, too,' I said.

Mrs Gill, who was sitting in a deckchair busy knitting, looked up. 'Be back here at five o'clock cos the train leaves at six.'

Mr Gill was having ten minutes' shut-eye, as he called it. After a heavy lunch of corned beef sandwiches, a plate of Southend-on-Sea cockles and, of course, a glass of his favourite Guinness, he had finally closed his eyes.

'Let's walk to the end of the pier,' Bob said.

'Can we come back on the train?' I asked.

'If we've enough money left,' he said. 'It would be nice to take home a little present for Mum. She'd be ever so pleased that we remembered to take her something back.'

'Gifts from Southend-on-Sea' read the sign. 'Let's look in here,' said Bob

'How about that?' I asked, pointing to a glass bowl.

'Don't be silly,' Bob said. 'We can't afford that.'

'This, then.'

'Oh, don't be daft – it's too much money. Ah, that's more like it,' he added as he spotted a tiny dish with 'Best Wishes from Southend-on-Sea'

inscribed on it. 'See, it's ninepence, and we can afford that.'

'I know she'll like it. Bet she puts it on her dressing-table. Can I carry it?'

'Put it in your pocket, and don't lose it, will you?' he said.

A train went rattling past as we made our way to the end of the pier. An aeroplane flew overhead trailing a banner that read 'Guinness for Strength'.

'Wonder what it's like to fly,' I asked.

Bob looked up too. 'I'd like to try it one day. . . Look, there's a paddle-steamer coming. Race you to the end of the pier!'

With my hand in my pocket over Mum's present, I chased after him.

'We can't afford that.'

The Silver Jubilee

'Oh knees up Mother Brown...'

'Sh! Sh! Do be quiet now, you boys,' Mum called out, as she switched on the wireless. 'Your Grandad was right when he used to say that he had never come across two such chatterboxes! Be quiet for five minutes.'

It was hard to do as she asked after all the fun and excitement of the long, early summer day. Looking out of the parlour window, as the sun went down over the rooftops and the street darkened, I watched as four grown-ups emptied their glasses, gathered around the piano and pushed it away up the street. The trestle tables and benches leaned against the railings outside the corner shop – only a few short hours before they had been laden with plates and dishes of sandwiches, buns and cakes, apples and oranges, jellies and ices. We had sat there with our paper hats, so excited, while the grown-ups had served us. We had watched Punch & Judy, and we had laughed and sung with the clown like the one from the circus that once a year came to Wanstead Flats, with his big red nose, baggy trousers and long, floppy boots that he kept tripping over. The piano had played, and the grown-ups had danced around it. They had enjoyed this day as much as we had. There had been loud cheers as Mrs Dixon came out of the shop carrying the biggest cake we had ever seen.

For weeks we had watched and endeavoured to help as our street corner had been transformed into a red, white and blue wonderland. Strings of flags criss-crossed the street from every bedroom window. We had watched old Dixon carefully arrange in a large gold frame in the corner shop window a picture of our King and Queen. A big Union Jack had been hung over the shop doorway, and bunting wrapped around the lamp-posts; even the old sewer wall had been painted red, white and blue.

But the great day that had taken weeks to prepare for had now come and gone. As it became darker I watched the man lean his bike against the street lamp and stand his ladder against it; then, as if by magic, all the red, white and blue came back to life again.

'Can you turn it up a bit louder?' Mum asked Bob, making herself comfortable in Grandad's old chair, and as we sat at the kitchen table we listened as the King's voice came out of the wireless.

'At the close of this memorable day I must speak to my people everywhere. . . I can only say to you, my dear people, that the Queen and I thank you from the depths of our hearts for all the loyalty and, may I say so, the love with which this day you have surrounded us. I dedicate myself anew to your service for all the years that may still be given me.'

The Blitz of 1940 demolished 'our corner', including Mr Dixon's corner shop and 40 or so cared-for little houses. Today a 14-storey tower block looks down on what was once our small corner of E13.

Those 'orrible things!

'Cos they dropped bombs on us in the Great War!'

Mr Chambers opened his street door, and as we passed by he came out on to the step to collect his empty dustbin. As he did so, we heard a soft whirring noise above us.

'Gee whiz, look at that!' We gazed and pointed up to the sky, and so too did half of the street.

'Crikey!' we shouted. 'We've never seen an airship before!'

It seemed to go straight down the street above us until it gradually disappeared from our sight, as silently and as quickly as it had come.

'Whadya think of that, Mr Chambers?' we asked him.

With his thumbs in his waistcoat he replied, ''orrible things they are, boys. Shouldn't be allowed.'

'But why, Mr Chambers?' we asked.

'Cos they dropped bombs on us in the Great War,' he declared. 'Don't know why they want to go up there,' he said, lifting his eyebrows. 'The Lord made it for the birds, and not for us. This is where we belong, boys, down 'ere.'

To emphasise his point he stamped his foot down on his step. 'And what with all these

aeroplanes, too. . .' he mumbled as he bent down over his dustbin. We left him to it, as Mrs Gill waved to us and closed her bedroom window, satisfied that there was nothing else to see.

It was dustbin day, and as the old horse-drawn dust-cart went slowly down our street it would soon be filled. We knew then that it would go up to the top where a big lorry with an empty dust-cart would be waiting. We joined the other lads as the empty cart was slowly winched down the iron rails that the driver, wearing big gloves, had pulled from beneath the lorry. He unhooked the wire from the cart and waited, wire and hook in his gloved hands, for the full cart to arrive.

Albie Gibbs nudged me and said, ''ere it comes.'

The full dust-cart arrived and the dustman unharnessed his horse.

'Come on old lad, it's your dinner time,' he said as he fixed the nosebag in place. The old horse tossed his head upwards with a snort and stamped his hoof on the asphalt in gratitude.

With the iron rails still in place at the back of the lorry, one of the waiting dustmen checked that the

iron lids on the dust-cart were firmly closed while the other picked up the wire cable, pulling it taut as he hooked it on to the full cart. The driver looked out of his cab.

'Right-o Charlie!' one of his mates called out. 'Take it up.'

We watched, fascinated, as the small iron wheels creaked and screeched up the rusty rails, and put our hands over our ears as the noise from the lorry's engine deafened us. Up and up went the cart until it reached the top, then with a jerk and a jolt it stopped. The dustman took his gloves off and banged on the lorry's cab door.

'Right-o Charlie, she's there.'

We took our hands from our ears as the street became quiet again.

'Come on, old boy,' said the dustman as he backed the horse into the shafts of the empty dust-cart. 'It's time we were off again.'

We all watched as he led him out into Balaam Street, the other dustmen walking alongside. As we walked back down the street reliving the excitement of the last few hours, Albie called out to the man clearing the drains in the gutter, 'Oi mister, can you see any of my marbles down there?'

The ones that got away

We were playing blow football on Aunt Liz's kitchen table when she came down the passage

The old slaughterhouse has gone, and that Victorian seat of learning, Holborn Road School, has suffered the same fate as my own school. A housing estate now occupies the whole area.

Aunt Liz's house still stands opposite, untouched and unchanged by two World Wars and the bulldozers. Her daughter, my cousin Doris, has lived in the house next door for as long as I can remember.

from the street door, saying, 'There's some animals got away from the slaughterhouse up the street! It looks as if they're coming this way!'

We forgot blow football and dashed out to see for ourselves. As cousin Billy opened the door two big pigs dashed past, pursued by grown-ups in overalls and wellingtons and brandishing sticks, followed closely by the crowd that had witnessed the escape! We stood by the gateway and joined in the cheers as they all dashed past and

disappeared down the street. There were more cheers as another two pigs refused to go through the slaughterhouse doors, but the cheers turned to jeers as they were prodded and pushed and ushered into the yard.

Later that afternoon as I walked home I thought of my Uncle Bob's pigs in far-away Staffordshire.

Uncle Bob was my Dad's eldest brother, a lovely roly-poly of an uncle, and every so often Uncle Bill took Mum, Bob and me to Euston station to get the train to Wolverhampton, and we stayed a week or so at Portobello visiting my Staffordshire aunts and uncles.

'Here come the two Cockney lads,' they said when we arrived.

Uncle Bob and Aunt Tiz lived in Granny Kimberley's old cottage in the High Street, and the big yard behind backed on to open fields. I heard Aunt Pearl say to Mum, as we all went in under the low front door that led into the parlour, 'Our Bob hasn't changed a thing since our Mum went.'

It looked as if the ceiling in the cheerful little room was being held up by all the pictures; you couldn't see any walls, the pictures were hung so close together. A big grandfather clock ticked away in the corner, knick-knacks, as Mum called them, filled every inch of

table and shelf space, and even in summer a fire burned brightly in the grate.

'Sit down,' Aunt Tiz said, but Uncle Bob was having none of that.

'Come and have a look at my pigs,' he said, so we followed him into the smelly, cobbled yard and peered over the old brick wall at his four fat pigs. He gave each of them

36

a gentle prod with his long cane, and with a grunt and a snort they came to the wall and fixed us with their tiny eyes, as much as to say, 'What are you two Cockney lads doing in our back yard?'

My eyes fixed on the medal that dangled from Uncle Bob's hunter watch chain. 'What's that for, Uncle Bob?'

'Eeh, haven't you see that afore?' he asked me. Bob and I shook our heads. He turned the medal for us to read the inscription. 'Your dad had one, yer know.' It read 'Willenhall Swifts, League Champs, South Staffs League, 1912'.

He led us into the kitchen, reached up to a dark shelf and laid an album on the table.

'There you are, lads,' he said, flicking over a page. 'There's yer Dad.' He pointed a finger at our Dad, seated in the front row of the Willenhall Swifts Football Team with a football at his feet. 'That's me next t'im, and there's your Uncle Sam.' He closed the musty smelling album. 'I'm certain your Mum must have 'is medal,' he said,

as he ushered us out of the kitchen and joined the others in the little parlour.

When we went up to bed later that evening I said to Bobby, 'I've been wondering if Uncle Bob sends his pigs to the slaughterhouse.'

'I hope he doesn't, cos if he does I don't want to go and see him again!'

Re-laying our cricket pitch

'Mister, they asked me to ask you, please can we have our cricket pitch back.'

When we came out of Harris's sweet shop and newsagents, sucking our Dickie Bird's choc-ices, we turned the corner and discovered heaps of granite chips lining the pavement on both sides of the street as far as our eyes could see, dotted with 'Road up' signs. As we walked down the street our black shoes became almost white from the dust from the chips.

'Gee whiz!' we exclaimed. 'These heaps weren't here this morning when we went off to school. What's happening?'

Walking along to the high brick wall where the northern outfall sewer made its way down to Becton, we stopped dead in our tracks and watched as workmen busily erected a large tarpaulin-covered hut, pulling and pushing the tarpaulin over the long metal framework. Tables and benches lay about on the pavement alongside it, shovels, wheelbarrows and pick-axes were stacked and lined up against the brick wall, and the red 'Road up' signs stood about, together with the whitewood tar barrels, heaps of coke and two carts piled with more granite chips. The horses, their nosebags in place, ignored us as we stared at it all.

There were also blackened tar tenders, with their long spindly chimneys, but in pride of place, next to the now erected hut, was the giant steam-roller, with its polished brass and silver embellishments and splendid shiny black and green paintwork.

'Cor, what a blooming' cheek,' Alf Barret said. 'They've only gone and pinched our cricket pitch.'

We sat on the railings, not knowing what to look at first. The men were wearing old sacks for aprons, their trousers tied up at the knees to keep them high up over their heavy hobnailed boots. In turn they placed their buckets on the ground beneath the tap at the end of the tar tender and, when it had gushed out, their heavy-gloved hands picked up the buckets and, bending low, they spread the tar over the road. Soon a large patch spread out across one side of the roadway, glistening and rippling like black treacle, while other men with long-handled, rubber broom-like implements smoothed and coaxed it, as directed by the man in the bowler hat.

Satisfied with their efforts, the foreman then summoned other men, who had until then been onlookers leaning on their shovels. They quickly got to work on the heaps of granite chips and shovelled a fine layer across the black tar. At another signal from the bowler hat, the steam-roller came down the street like a roll of thunder; it looked like a big toy, puffing and wheezing, with black, oily smoke coming from its tall chimney as it edged towards the scattered chips.

With much skill, turning handles and wheels as if he had more than two hands, the driver guided the gentle giant backwards and forwards.

'All right, Will!' the bowler hat called. 'That'll do.'

Nipper from the top of the street went by, holding a cup with both hands.

'What 'ave you got there, Nipper?' Albie Gibbs asked him.

'I've been to Dixon's to get a cupful of pickles for my mum,' he replied.

''ere, do us a favour, Nip,' said Albie. 'Ask 'im, that one with the bowler hat, how much longer they're going to be down our street.'

'Oh, all right,' said Nipper.

Albie took the cupful of pickles from Nip, saying, ''ere, I'll hold it in case you drop it.'

Above all the noise and bustle we heard Nipper say to the bowler hat, ''ere mister, they asked me to ask you 'ow much longer are you going to be down our street, cos we want our cricket pitch back, please.'

We saw the bowler hat wave a large finger at him. 'Cricket, cricket pitch? This road of mine's for lorries, 'orses and carts and motors, not for you and your cricket, Sonny

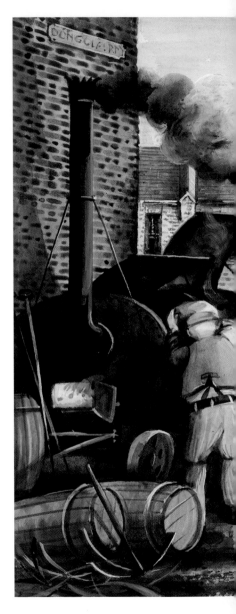

Jim. Now 'op it,' and turning to us added, 'the lot of yer.'

Albie chased after Nipper. 'Oi, Nipper, don't forget yer Mum's pickles.'

The Woolwich Free Ferry

Waiting for the tram to Wanstead Flats, Eddy said, 'I haven't a penny for the fare today.'

'Nor 'ave I,' said Albie.

'Well, what's the use of waiting here then?' the rest of us exclaimed.

'I know,' I said. 'Let's go to Woolwich. We can ride on the ferry cos it's free.'

The trees and the ponds on the Flats were quickly forgotten as we all set off for Woolwich. Hurrying past the soap and gas works at Becton we held our noses. Cor, what a pong!

Shortly after, poking up amongst the chimney-pots, we could see ships' masts and brightly painted funnels. Cranes, like fingers, pointed up to the sky above the roof-tops, and instead of the soap factory we could smell Old Father Thames. We forget the long walk in our excitement, hurrying around the last corner.

'Look, the ferry's in!' we all shouted. 'Hurry up – we don't want to miss it.'

With that there was a rush for the gangway. All out of breath, we decided that we would go up by the paddle-wheel first and go down and see the wonders of the engine room on the return trip. We climbed up beside it.

'Oi, you lads down there! Mind you behave or I'll have you ashore.'

'Aye-aye, Cap'n,' answered cheeky Albie Gibbs.

The view took our breath away – ships and boats of all shapes and sizes as far as our eyes could see, screeching seagulls and sails. Oh, this was lots more fun than Wanstead Flats!

'Look, I bet those bobbies are after Doctor Fu Manchu down at Limehouse,' said Alf, as a river police launch sped by.

Boom, boom, boom – the paddle-wheel began to turn and the water frothed up below us as we set off for distant shores.

And as Grandad used to say, '"Across the water" was like being in a foreign land, cos they don't even speak the King's English across there.'

We dashed back through the tunnel under the river to meet the ferry when it got to the other side.

Old Chambers's fanlight

Alfie Barret bowled a fast one at me...

I looked at the clock on the mantelpiece. It was a quarter to seven. Putting my jacket on I looked around the door into the parlour where Bob was doing his homework.

'I'm going up to the top to meet Mum.'

He looked up with a grin and said, 'What have you been up to today?'

'Oh, nothing,' I replied.

But Bob knew that any worries I had I took up to the bus stop.

'Mum. . .' Taking a deep breath, in a rush I said, 'I broke Mr Chambers's fanlight this evening.'

Alf Barret

Forty pairs of eyes looked up as Mr Lethaby, our headmaster, opened the door of class 1a.

'Here's the young man I talked to you about, Mr Murray. I am sure he will do well in your class.'

Alf made his way to a vacant desk. Charlie Mount nudged me, saying, 'You know 'im, don't you? He lives down Dongola Road.'

And so began a friendship that has lasted for 60 years or more. We played all the street games. Football, cricket, hot rice, Oi Jimmy Knacker, Knocking down Ginger and so many others, and in doing so collected our share of bumps and bruises, and a few broken windows!

Long hot summer days were spent on the Flats at Wanstead, providing we could find a penny for the fare! If not, we went to'ing and fro'ing on the Woolwich Free Ferry, or tiddler fishing down at Becton. Cold winter Saturday mornings were spent on the football pitches down Prince Regent Lane. When we meet now, our talk soon turns to those carefree boyhood days.

At 14, with our long 'uns on, we travelled on the same tram to the city, Alf to his office job in Aldgate and me to my office boy's job in Clerkenwell. When the time came Alf joined the Army and crossed the Channel with the South Wales Borderers in the months following D-Day, Alf served in Belgium, Holland and Germany. Demobbed in 1947, we met up again soon after.

His enthusiasm for sports is as strong as ever, although these days he plays from the comfort of his armchair! Married with children and grandchildren, Alf retired as a sales administration manager with an international company in 1991.

Old Tom Lethaby down at Balaam Street would have been delighted with Alf's achievements since that distant day when he ushered him into class 1a; and I was forever grateful to him, because Alf's been a good friend ever since!

'Oh Kenny, how did you do that?'

'Well, we was playing cricket and using the lamp-post opposite his door as a wicket. Alfie Barret bowled a fast one at me, the ball hit my bat, and it went straight through his fanlight.'

'I don't know why you must play in the street when you have the park around the corner.'

'I know, Mum, but Old Parky chases us out sometimes.'

'Well, what did Mr Chambers say then?'

'Er, well, I dunno – we all ran off.'

She stopped, and for the first time looked cross. 'Kenny, you should have knocked on his door and owned up that it was you that did it.'

I felt miserable and looked it. 'I know, Mum, but I scarpered with everybody else.'

We carried on up the street.

'Well,' she said. 'I'll have to go round and see him when we've laid the table for supper – and pay for it.'

'Oh thanks, Mum.'

However, my relief was short-lived when she said, 'Mind you, you'll have to come with me.'

Mum knocked at his door. I looked up and saw that a piece of plywood had been tacked over the fanlight. I looked down at the step as the door opened.

'Hello Mr Chambers,' Mum said. 'My Ken wants to say sorry for breaking your fanlight and not knocking and telling you that it was him that did it. He knows he shouldn't have run off like he did.'

Old Chambers's black cat walked out from behind his legs and looked up at me as if to say, 'Ah, you're the one, are you?' Blooming old cat, he was always in our back yard, scratching up the flower seeds that

Mum sowed in the springtime. I often chased him off, and he would leap up on to our fence, jump down into Mrs Golding's and see what he would get up to there!

'Well, Mrs Kimberley, boys will be boys, and I suppose we were all young once,' he said with a smile, and looking at me added, 'though I can't remember when.'

'Well, when you have the fanlight put in, let me know how much it is,' Mum said.

'I will,' he replied. 'Don't worry about it. Goodnight Mrs Kimberley. Goodnight young fella-me-lad.'

I was thankful that the interview was over. As we turned the corner I said to Mum, 'Mr Chambers is a nice old man.'

'Yes, he got your dad a job in Becton gas works when we came back from Staffordshire to live with your Gran and Grandad.'

When we went upstairs to bed that night, I said to Bob, 'Why did Mum and Dad come back from Staffordshire to live here with Gran and Grandad?'

He had to think for a moment.

'Well, I believe after they were married he took our Mum back to his home to live, but couldn't find any work there.'

'But why did he die?' I asked, as he put the light out and climbed into bed.

'Oh, Mum will tell you all about it when you're older. Goodnight, Ken.'

'Goodnight, Bobby.'

Scrumping

It had been raining heavily and there were too many puddles on the road for any of our favourite street games! We were sitting on the iron railings outside the corner shop.

'Look at those!' we exclaimed, as we watched Mrs Dixon arrange a trayful of glossy toffee apples in the shop window. Moments later Mr Dixon appeared in the window, and placed a card alongside the tray – '1d each'. It was toffee apple time, and to bite through the thick coating of dark glossy toffee into a juicy and usually sour apple was a joy! Stuck on a stick, you could nibble away at it for hours on end.

'Ah,' said Albie, 'my Mum makes bigger and better ones than those – and they don't cost me nuffink.'

'Oh yeah?' we all exclaimed. 'Tell us how she makes the toffee then, and where she gets the apples from.'

'Cor, it's my Mum's secret how she makes the toffee,' he replied, adding very mysteriously, 'but I know where to get the apples.'

Charlie Mount pushed his soapbox on pram wheels down Balaam Street. We followed alongside. We turned into gloomy Barber's Alley and Albie whispered, 'It's just down 'ere.'

We were on familiar ground because the alley passed our school playground, which was now all quiet and deserted. On the other side, wooden fences and brick walls concealed yards, gardens and sheds. In the gloom Albie stopped; hanging over the wall were the biggest, most luscious green apples you ever saw!

''ere, keep a look-out,' he said to me and Podgy. We did as he asked. Looking left and right I could see that the pavement was dark and deserted. Only the lamp-light reflected up on to the juicy, round apples as we all sat about helping ourselves. Occasionally a light flicked on and off in a nearby window, a dog barked, or a cat paused on its way up the alley to see what we were up to, but we had little time to notice or to hear. I turned and could see that

Charlie's box on wheels was almost full to the top. As the apples came down left, right and centre, I peeped round the corner again.

'Oh crikey!' I called out. ''ere comes Sergeant Ebbage!' There was a frantic scramble to scarper. We ran off so fast with Charlie's box that one of the pram wheels came off, and the lop-sided box skidded down the alleyway, our juicy apples going in all directions over the paving stones. It came to rest by the school gate.

A few days later, during the mental arithmetic lesson, Mr Lethaby came into the classroom.

'Mr Murray, I would like to have a word with your class, please.'

'Of course, Mr Lethaby, of course.' Mr Murray turned to Alf, saying, 'Sit down, Barret.' Alf was on his feet at his desk to tell us all as quickly as possible what 8 times 12 was, then add the answer to 19! He sat down with a grin and some relief.

Mr Lethaby went on. 'It has been brought to my attention that on an evening a few days ago it was thought that boys from this school brought disgrace on themselves. They may not have been in this class, but I have a strong feeling for various reasons that they are.'

Charlie nudged me with his foot under the desk. We had a good idea what Old Lethaby was going on about!

Barber's Alley remains in places as it was, although smart new lights have replaced the lone gas-lamp of my day, and tarmac has replaced the stone paving. The adjacent tram sheds have gone, replaced by new housing. Of the apple tree we plundered there is no sign!

'It's one thing to go out scrumping for a few apples. Even Mr Murray and I were guilty of that in our younger days.' We all laughed at this, but he held up his hand, all stern again. 'But I won't have and will not tolerate scrumping by the soapbox load. It's

just not playing the game. Now is that clearly understood? It's just not cricket.'

The whole class said together, 'Yes, sir.'

As he opened the door to leave he turned and said, 'And by the way, the school caretaker has informed me that there is a soapbox and two pram wheels leaning against the gateway into Barber's Alley. Will the boy who owns them take them away. Otherwise they will go into the dustbin.'

We kicked our ball round the playground, then, when it was deserted, we sauntered out of the gate, hastily picking up a pram wheel each. We left Charlie to pick up the remains of his soap box and hurried off home.

Floodlit football

'Oi, butter-fingers! You'll never play for West Ham!' called out Podgy as Ed let in goal number 14.

On dry winter evenings school was forgotten, wireless was for grown-ups, last week's *Wizard* and *Hotspur* had been read and read and read again. The street lamp-posts served as our floodlights and goalposts, as did the opposite kerbstones. Light spilling from the parlour windows completed the scene.

The teams were picked and formalities were dispensed with – no referees, no half-time, no boos, no cheers, just an hour, perhaps two, of honest endeavour and magic. Was he a scout in disguise, we often wondered, as our lone spectator watched from behind the tea and coffee stall across the street. After all, that was how Dixie Dean was discovered, and now he played for England and earned £10 a week.

'Eddy, are you coming in?' Ed's mum stood on her doorstep. 'Your supper's ready on the table. I 'ope you haven't got your best Sunday shoes on!'

The spell was broken, and shoulders dropped for the first time in a couple of hours as Ed trooped away. In ones and twos we followed him to our own doorsteps. It was all over for another night, and as the street became deserted the 'scout' left the coffee stall and set off on his beat...

Our newsagent and the surrounding houses went during the Blitz, and the tram lines, stone sets and lamp-post are also long gone. New homes, an elderly people's day centre and modern street lighting make it all so unrecognisable from 60 or so years ago. Is this really the spot where we enjoyed our floodlit football?

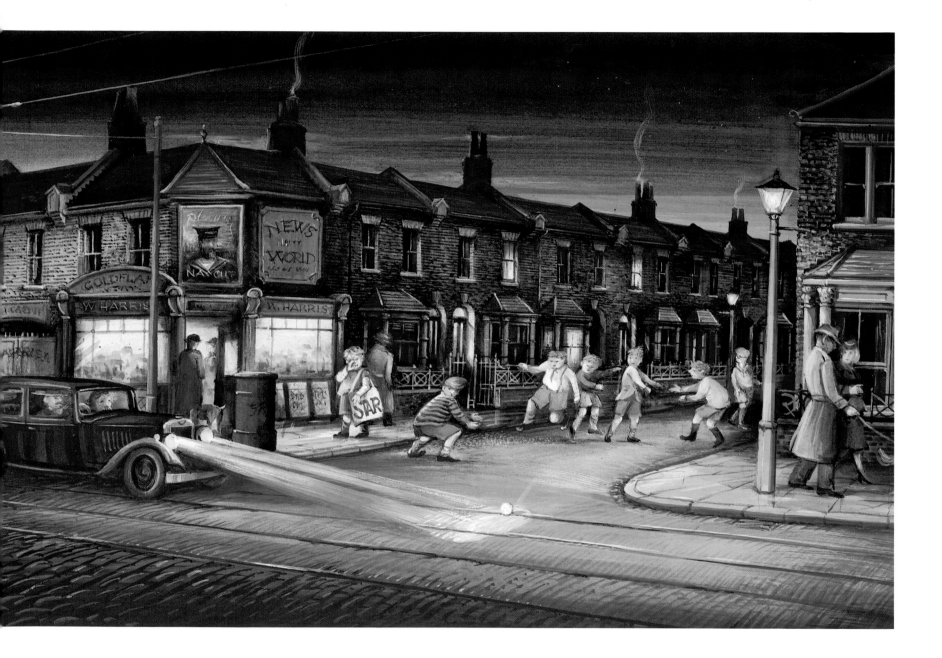

Saturday afternoon

'Move along there, there's room for one more on this row.'

Early one Saturday afternoon we had to make up our minds.

'Let's toss up for it.'

We always settled our differences in this manner. Charlie delved into his pocket, producing the inevitable assortment of pieces of string, a chipped five-stone, a few faded and crumpled cigarette cards, and, at long last, the sought-after penny.

'Stand back then.'

It was Charlie's penny, so we did as he asked.

'Heads it's the pictures, tails it's the Hammers.'

He tossed it up in the air; hitting the ground, it rolled steadily towards the drain hole in the gutter. I hastily put my foot out and stopped its progress. Gingerly lifting my shoe, we all gazed down.

'It's the pictures.'

We made our way to the Greengate Picture Palace and joined the queue.

'Cor, look, it's Tom Mix and his wonder horse, and Rin Tin Tin. Popeye as well.'

'Move along, move along, and have your money ready,' announced the man in the red coat, peaked cap and white gloves. I anxiously felt for the three pennies in my pocket. The fourth was for a bag of peanuts. Arriving at the cash box, we pushed our threepences through the arched hole in the glass screen. Anxious hands pushed aside the red curtain, and at last we were inside.

We hurried down the gangway to the nearest row of empty seats. Albie Gibbs playfully tipped the boys' caps off in the row in front of us.

'Oi there, no skylarkin' about!' another peaked cap called out.

There was now a great deal of excitement and expectancy around us as the seats became full. Slowly the lights dimmed. A great hush fell all round. All eyes looked to the front, but mine strayed to the painted walls, and as the lights dimmed further is seemed that the paintings sprang to life. Arabs in long, flowing robes sat by their tents grouped around a silver oasis. Camels looked into the distant desert. Galleons with

The Greengate Picture Palace as we knew it closed long ago. Years of bingo, billiards and snooker have come and gone, and today it all looks in a sorry state of disrepair, that little 'palace' where we cheered our heroes, booed the baddies and laughed at Laurel & Hardy and Popeye.

billowing sails sped over the waves and cruel-looking pirates with long, black beards and earrings were digging for buried treasure beneath waving palms. And was that Robin Hood and his Merry Men hiding up in those trees? Perhaps one day I would paint

pictures like these – Old Mr Solly at school says I've got to keep practising.

The now near darkness was stabbed by torchlight.

'Move along, move along. There's room for one more on this row.'

'Oh no there's not!' we all chorused, 'cos there's a seat missing.'

'Well one of you will have to sit on the floor!' bellowed the torch.

We all squeezed up. There was a desperate cry from the end of the row as Albie, with arms and legs flailing, was pushed off his seat.

Albie was forgotten as the silver screen flickered into life, revealing our heroes in desperate trouble. Then a fine mist descended all over us. Cor, what a pong!

'It's only the flitgun ladies,' said a voice from the dark, adding, 'My Uncle Jack said they don't call the old Greengate the fleapit for nothing!'

Among the cheers and boos and crackle of peanut shells, all else was forgotten as Tom Mix rode up to the rescue.

Winkles and shrimps

'All things bright and beautiful...'

I hurried up the passage in my Sunday best and opened the street door.

'Hello Auntie Jessie, hello Auntie Em.'

Every so often Mum invited her two old friends to Sunday tea. They weren't my real aunts, but Mum said Bob and I should call them that, as they had often bought us toys when we were both very young. They had all known each other for a long time, since working in the powder shed, as Mum called it, at the Woolwich Arsenal during the Great War. Mum was with Jessie when she met Dad on the Monkey Parade, as they called it, while he was waiting for discharge from the local barracks from the Army in 1918.

They greeted each other like long-lost friends, although they still worked together at old Mr Silberstein's in Mare Street, Hackney. They were just two of Mum's 30 'girls', as she called them, who on every day of the week except Sunday made their way by tram or bus to Mare Street. Mum was the 'forelady' and we knew off by heart such well-worn phrases as 'Molly's machine broke down today and she won't earn a penny until it's fixed', 'Jenny's belt broke and that old misery of a mechanic took his time to fix it', or 'Ada got her finger under her machine today'. As Mum said, 'her girls' were all on piece work, and didn't earn a penny if they were sitting idle at their machine.

Bob and I looked from one to the other as they related the week's ups and downs, old Silberstein getting it in the neck for most of the downs. On the mat in front of the fire old Paddy turned over and went back to sleep.

'You've painted the kitchen out, have you Adge?' Mum's name was Harriet, but everybody called her Adge except Auntie Edie.

'Yes, our Lizzie's Bill did it for me. He's got a lovely shine on it all,' she said, running her hand over the glossy dresser top.

'Who did the fancy bits in the corners?'

'Oh, our Bob and Ken did those for me. It was a lovely surprise when I came home and saw what they'd been up to.'

It was Bob's idea. He'd seen it in a book, so where there was room in the corners of each wall he sketched a posy of flowers, with trails of leaves coming from each. We each stood on a chair, Bob with his brushes carefully filling in the pencil marks, and me next to him holding up the little pots of poster paint like we used to use at school.

'I hope Mum likes it,' he had said a bit anxiously. She hadn't notice at first, but when she did, she said, 'Oh, I bet nobody down the street has a kitchen like mine.'

'Sit in the parlour,' Mum said to her two friends. 'There's a nice fire in there, while I lay the table for tea.'

'We'll help you,' they both said.

'No, no,' Mum replied. 'Bobby and Ken will help me. Oh, there's Harry Ponder outside. Take a shilling off the mantelpiece and ask him for a pint of winkles and a pint of shrimps. I know they like them for Sunday tea.'

As I was closing the street door, the Salvation Army band, who were paying the street a visit, struck up 'All Things Bright and Beautiful'. As they did so Auntie Em put a sixpence in my hand.

'There you are, my little lad, pop across and put it in their box for me.'

The kitchen table was laid with Mum's best Sunday tea-set. A cake stood proudly on the cake-stand with smaller fancy cakes around it, a plateful of bread and butter stood next to a dish of strawberry jam, sticks of celery stood up out of a glass vase, and Mum found space for the two bowls of Harry Ponder's winkles and shrimps. She carefully placed Gran's gleaming silver cruet among it all. Satisfied she said, 'Tell your Aunt Em and Aunt Jessie that tea's ready.'

'Cor, that looks lovely, Adge,' they said.

Then we all sat down and tucked in. Paddy nudged me under the table, and I quietly offered him half of my fancy cake!

Later they made themselves comfortable round the fire in the

parlour. We thought old Silberstein's ears must have been burning as we got on with our ludo and snakes and ladders.

'Shall I put a record on, Mum?' Bob asked. He wound up the gramophone.

'Put on the Gracie Fields one,' said Mum.

'Oh, I like Our Gracie,' the others exclaimed.

When the fire burned low in the grate, Auntie Jessie said, 'Well, we should be getting off home. I wish we had a cosy little house like this, don't you, Em? Instead of that old flat of ours in the buildings up at Shoreditch.'

'You will one day,' said Mum.

We said our goodbyes at the gate, and the aunts pressed a sixpence into each of our hands.

'Cor, thanks,' we said. Auntie Em reached up as far as she could and gave us each a big kiss. Auntie Jessie bent down and gave us a hug. We left them at the gate with

Mum, and hurried into the kitchen to switch on the wireless. The Palm Court Orchestra had finished. Bob fiddled with one of the three knobs and amongst the fading music and crackling noises a voice said, 'And now we bring you the fourth instalment of . . .' The voice faded in the

interference. Old Paddy raised himself off the hearth mat, stretched and yawned, and settled himself down beside Bob on Grandad's favourite fireside chair, as we listened wide-eyed to another hair-raising instalment of that villain from Limehouse, Doctor Fu Manchu!

Bunking in at Upton Park

Titch said, 'Help me bunk in, mister!'

We hurried along the Barking Road. It was early yet, but the trams and buses were full, and bikes, some with a passenger on the crossbar, were all going in the same direction. Podgy Comber came out of his father's barber shop and joined us on the way to Upton Park.

The Hammers were at home this Saturday, and we were all off to the match. Queues had started to form as we walked down Castle Street, and bikes were being stored in people's passageways, already overflowing on to the pavements outside. It was overcast, and rain threatened.

'There'll be plenty of raincoats about,' Albie said.

This meant that our chances of 'bunking in' today looked very rosy indeed. Sergeant Ebbage, who was at his customary place at the head of the queue, always turned a blind eye to our carryings on. Grandad used to say that this was because they were old sparring partners. At one o'clock the wooden doors rumbled aside. Click, click went the turnstile. The queue edged forwards.

Nudging Titch, Albie said, 'Try 'im, Titch.'

Titch looked up at the first

Sergeant Ebbage

'I'll fetch Sergeant Ebbage,' Grandad would say if Bob and I had been getting up to any mischief, a threat that was enough to stop us dead in our tracks! When we were both younger it used to be 'I'll fetch the bogy-man', and we would hide in the lavatory in the yard to keep out of his way.

Sergeant Ebbage lived in the house at the end of our yard. Mum said he had been a friend of Grandad's for many years. In his off-duty hours in the summer he and Grandad and a few other mates would sit outside the Greengate and quench their thirsts,

and, as Gran used to say, 'put the world to rights'.

His head and shoulders would tower above the fence as he went about tending his flowers. Spotting me he would stop, place his two big hands on top of the fence, peer down at me and say, ''ullo, young fella-me-lad. Pop indoors and tell your Grandad I'll be going up to the top in ten minutes.'

I would hurry indoors and deliver his message. Grandad would reach up and get his straw hat off the peg. I wonder what they're going to put right today, I thought!

The Bobby Moore Stand towers over the home of West Ham FC at Upton Park and what little remains of Castle Street. New buildings have replaced the terraced houses, where for tuppence you could store your bike while you went in to the match. Alf and I debate our chances of 'bunking in' today!

raincoat in the queue. 'Help me bunk in, mister.'

Before mister had time to blink, Titch had comfortably positioned himself inside the generous raincoat that almost reached to the ground.

Being taller than Titch it was more difficult for me, but I made myself comfortable beneath the next raincoat. Alfie Barret followed, but not before he had asked the bobby if his horse could go as fast as Tom Mix's.

For Titch life was simple. For the rest of us the vital moment came as the click, click came round. Bent double with knees on the ground and head tucked in I scrambled in beneath the last click! In the gloom and dust among the boots and shoes I straightened and scrambled up the concrete steps where we were all soon lost with the grown-ups. A patch of blue sky peeped through and the sun shone on the immaculate stretch of green, with its carefully ruled white lines. It had stopped raining. 'When Irish eyes are smiling,' sang the loudspeakers.

'Here they come!' the cry went up, and we joined in with the rest of them!

Mosley on the Broadway

Only the passing trams normally disturbed the pigeons.

I stooped down and looked at the knob on the YZ chewing-gum machine. With every fourth penny it gave two packets of spearmint instead of the customary one. Unbeknown to everybody, including old Dixon and everybody else except his chosen mates, Charlie Mount had scratched a mark on the knob,

indicating when the fourth turn was due. We were the chosen few, and we would wait around the machine until the mark indicated that the next penny would produce two packets. On this occasion it wasn't in the right position, so I put my penny back in my trouser pocket and joined the other lads sitting on the railings outside the corner shop. Albie hurried around the corner.

''ere,' he said, 'old Mosley's up on the Broadway with 'is Blackshirts. There's lots of shouting and fighting. Come one, let's go and watch.'

Having nothing better to do we followed him up to the Broadway. As we got closer we could hear the hollering and shouting.

'Come on,' Albie said, as he

started to run. 'We don't want to miss anything.'

There was not much chance of that, because this evening the Broadway was a heaving mass of grown-ups punching and kicking each other! It was normally a quiet and peaceful spot, the public library on the far side taking pride of place. Only the passing trams disturbed the pigeons.

Little has changed on the Broadway. The library looks as it always did, although the Prince Albert seems to have undergone a facelift. I remember more trees, removed no doubt to make way for the new traffic islands! As this photograph was being taken, two young lads across the street turned their backs on us, dropped their trousers and showed us their brown bottoms. Seems that they're still as cheeky as ever in E13!

'How do they know who to punch?' somebody said.

'Gee whiz, it's like something out of the Keystone Kops,' said another.

Even a passing tram driver was caught up in it all, as he grappled with a roughneck who had dared to put a foot on his tram! We all

cheered as, just like the pictures and in the nick of time, the mounted police came galloping up. Mosley and his mates seemed to remain aloof from the bedlam; high above everybody with their banners and raised arms, they seemingly encouraged everybody to greater efforts on their behalf. The black Maria was doing a roaring trade as scrapper after scrapper was frog-marched towards it, while coppers' hats flew and lay everywhere!

'Crikey, see who that is!' we all exclaimed, not believing our eyes.

'Gosh, it's Steppo. What's he doing there?' we asked, as he was bundled up the steps into the black Maria! Above all the hullabaloo, we heard his appealing cry, 'I wasn't in it! Me and me Dad got off the tram and some bloke 'it 'im, and I was standing there looking for 'im.'

'Well, Sonny Jim, perhaps you'll find him in our Maria, so up you go,' said the copper.

Cor, we thought, poor old Steppo, always up to his neck in it. Don't know what our headmaster's going to say when he finds out at school tomorrow.

The night watchman

'Come on you lads, time you were off home and in bed.'

Mr Cohn locked up the cupboard from where Ernie and I had sold pencils, exercise books, rulers and everything else during the two hours of night-school.

'You can go now, lads. Goodnight.'

Some weeks before, as we were leaving Mr Cohn's history lesson, he had called out, 'You two boys, Bright and Kimberley. I want a word with you both. My night-school classes are starting soon and I want two lads to help me. You two will be fine. Report to me on Monday, Tuesday and Thursday at 7pm sharp.' Looking at us over those small glasses that always looked as if they were about to fall off the end of his nose, he added, 'Off you go now,' and we did as we were told.

We chased across the playground as it was a cold winter's evening, and both hurried down Barber's Alley.

'I know, let's have a warm at the night watchman's hut. I know where he'll be.'

We passed the steam-roller, which now lay silent for the night, the tar tenders with their fireboxes open, the hot coals that had been raked out still smouldered on the ground. From their tall chimneys a wisp of smoke went up to the cold night sky. The hurricane lamps that were dotted along the street flickered brightly. Passing the tar barrels, upturned wheelbarrows and 'Road up' signs, we felt the comforting warmth of the coke brazier as we approached the watchman's hut. The smell of hot coke, tar and paraffin descended on us like a thick blanket.

Albie and Alf had already made themselves comfortable on the bench opposite the watchman, while Eddy and Charlie with arms outstretched warmed their hands from a comfortable distance.

The watchman puffed away happily on his clay pipe, enjoying, it seemed, the young company around him. With a few deft taps on the table with his pipe and a quick wipe across his moustache with the back of his hand, he cleared his throat.

'Well, lads, did I ever tell you of the Balaam Street ghost tram?'

He paused, making sure he had our attention. Albie and Alf, now with their elbows on the table, rested their heads between their hands; Ernie edged forwards and I followed, and Eddy and Charlie, now as warm as toast, moved closer to the watchman turned storyteller. We were all ears.

'It was like this 'ere,' he said. 'It was midnight. I knew it was, cos St Andrew's had just struck the hour. I heard a tram come up over the bridge. Listen – just like that.'

Sure enough we all heard the familiar sound of a tram on its way to the docks. He let this information sink in. We all edged closer.

'Strange,' he said. 'I thought, being 12 o'clock they should all be in the sheds in Greengate Street at this time of night.' He paused again. We all edged closer still.

'I was sitting on his very bench when it passed by, all lit up like.' He waved his hands above his head, as if it was passing by at that very moment. 'Full of soldier boys it was, all laughing they were, with their kitbags and uniforms all shining brightly. All singing they were: "Goodbye Piccadilly, farewell Leicester Square".' He drummed out the imaginary tune with fingers on the tabletop.

'Good Gawd!' he exclaimed. 'I could see right through them, tram an' all.' He rummaged around in his waistcoat and produced a tiny bottle from a pocket, taking a quick nip. 'I had to have a little drop of this, I don't mind telling you,' he said.

Albie broke the long silence. 'Cor, didn't anybody else see it?'

'See it? See it? It's only us night watchmen can see things like that, when everybody else is tucked up in bed for the night. I tell you, as sure as I'm sitting here it was just like one of the old trams that took the soldier boys down to the docks on their way to Flanders in the war!'

We all jumped out of our skins as Sergeant Ebbage came up out of the darkness.

'Come on, lads, come on. Time you were all home and in bed, cos you'll be late for school in the morning. And what yarn has old Billy been spinning you tonight?'

We all huddled together as we set off down the cold, empty street. I glanced back and saw old Ebbage making himself comfortable on the bench in front of the brazier. The watchman offered him his box of matches and they both lit up their pipes. We went our different ways and hurried off home.

Mum came in from the scullery. 'Did they have trams during the Great War?' I asked her.

'Oh, I can't remember all that long time ago,' she replied. 'But why do you ask?'

Guy Fawkes

'Penny for the guy, please, mister...?'

It was Friday afternoon, and from my desk I could look through the fanlight over the classroom door and see the clock that was on the wall above Mr Lethaby's desk. It was a quarter past three. Any minute now I knew Mr Murray would call, 'Kimberley, pin this up on the hall noticeboard.' As well as our teacher he was the sports master, and he selected the senior and junior school football teams.

Every Saturday morning during the playing season he would be with us at one or other of the numerous playing fields that were available to us all, encouraging us, bullying us. But at the end of it all, win or lose, he would always say, 'Well done, lads,' and would be off to catch his bus. He was much liked and respected by us all. When he'd gone we in turn chased off and treated ourselves to a halfpenny glass of hot blackcurrant juice and, if we could find another halfpenny, a dry crusty roll.

Pinning up the notice, I of course always looked for my name first. It was a relief to see it, especially in the senior team. I always thought that it was because I was tall and not for my playing ability that my name appeared with regularity.

I glanced at the names I knew would always be there – Horace Smith and Arnold Eve – who both at that time played for the West Ham boys team. This we all strove

to do, but only the very best and the fortunate gifted few pulled on the famous jersey. They were my schoolboy heroes, along with Len Goulden of course, who played for West Ham United proper and was now an England international player. In his schooldays he played for Holborn, the team that my cousin Billy now played for.

I looked at the clock again. It was half past three. As I did so old Murray called out, 'Right lads, pack up now.'

This was customary because the last half-hour of Friday afternoons was devoted to 'topics of the day', as he called it.

But what about the football team notice, I thought. Mr Murray walked across to the blackboard and wrote in large capital letters 'GUY FAWKES AND THE GUNPOWDER PLOT'. He turned round to us all and said, 'I almost forgot – football's off tomorrow. The pitches at Prince Regent Lane are waterlogged.'

There were ahs and ohs from the lads in the classroom who were involved, including me. Ignoring our disappointment, Mr Murray was now more interested in finding out what we knew of Guy Fawkes.

'Kimberley, stand up and tell the class about Guy Fawkes.'

Mr Fawkes was furthest from my mind at that moment, fed up that there was no football tomorrow, but I rose slowly to my feet, conscious of all eyes on me.

'Er, well, er, oh, he tried to blow up the Houses of Parliament,' I blurted out, with some relief.

'When was this?' he asked me.

'Er, well. . .' I did know the date because history was one of my favourite lessons, but the date on this Friday afternoon just wouldn't come.

'Well, was it last month? Last year?' Of course, all the clever-clogs around me sniggered at this. Then it all came out in a rush.

'On 1605, sir, and he was executed in the Tower of London, sir, in 1606.'

I was pleased with myself, as he told me to sit down.

'Bright, tell the class why Guy Fawkes tried to blow up Parliament.' I didn't envy my mate Ernie!

As I walked home from school with Alf and Charlie, the latter said, 'I'm taking my guy up to the top tonight.' We agreed that we would go along with him.

It was dark and misty when we knocked at Charlie's door. His guy sat in a barrow that his elder brother had made, its long legs hanging over the edge. A scruffy bowler hat was perched on top of a Guy Fawkes mask, and two fat arms with gloves tied to the ends clutched a notice that read 'Please spare a copper for the guy'.

We admired Charlie's handiwork, helped him push the barrow to the top and found the best spot

opposite the tram and bus stop. Next door was the tobacconist's. It was a very good time as all the grown-ups were coming home from work. It wasn't long before we were busy asking, 'Please spare a copper for the guy, mister.'

Alf, too, was busy outside the tobacconist's shop. 'Can I have the cigarette card, please?' adding, 'and a copper for the guy?' as he waylaid

men opening their newly bought packets of Players. We all envied Alf, who had the best collection of cigarette cards in the school. Cricketers, film stars, footballers, he had them all!

Albie Gibbs was making his voice heard above ours, as he hustled and bustled amongst the grown-ups.

'Blooming cheek,' exclaimed Charlie. 'He ain't got a guy. He's using ours!'

Seeing us and our guy, he hurried over. 'It's all right if I use yours, is it? Cos I couldn't find any old clothes this year to make one.'

Alf said with a laugh, 'Just stand there, Albie,'cos you'll do as you are!'

The early mist had turned now to fog, and most of the workers were home having their tea. The tobacconist closed his door. We stood around the guy, each counting his 'takings', Albie included. It added up to two shillings and sixpence. Charlie had half as it was his guy, and we carefully gave each other fivepence each.

I left them at the corner and went home.

On the big night we went to Aunt Liz's to enjoy ourselves round their bonfire. Uncle Jim would call in with a box of fireworks to add to our collection, and Uncle Bill would carefully let off the thunder flashes and Roman candles while Billy and me dashed about with our sparklers. For a lark Mum would let off a jumping cracker behind Uncle Bill.

Quarter to nine

'Call that a conker?' he said as he swaggered off.

Taking the big fat conker out of the jar of vinegar, I thought to myself, 'Cor, I've got a champion there!' I threaded the string through the hole made with a meat skewer and tied two big knots in it. Giving it a whirl, I imagined that I could knock any other conker out of sight. When Uncle Jim had called in to see us, he had told me of his conker-playing days at Balaam Street School.

'Keep it in vinegar for a day or two,' he had said. 'After that give it a good polish up with your mum's lino polish to give it a nice shine. Take my tip, boy, and you'll have a winner.'

I put the duster and polish back under the sink in the scullery. The conker gleamed as I put it in my pocket. Looking at the clock on the mantelpiece I thought, 'Crikey! It's quarter to nine.'

We didn't waste the walk to school but enjoyed these last moments of freedom, practising our skills, be it at marbles, dribbling with a tennis ball or, my latest favourite, conkers. Coming down the street I spotted the reigning conker champ.

'Play you?' I asked him.

'Yes,' he said. 'I want the first hit though.'

'Oh, all right,' I replied. I smiled to myself as I looked at the gleaming conker at the end of my piece of string. It looked indestructible.

The champ brought his conker down on mine with an almighty wallop. I couldn't believe my eyes. I was left holding just a bit of string. My fat, rosy conker lay in pieces on the pavement.

'Call that a conker,' he said, as he swaggered off to school.

'Cor,' I thought. 'Just wait till I see my Uncle Jim.'

Passing the chewing-gum machine outside the corner shop, I saw that Charlie Mount's scratch on the knob was in the right place to deliver two packets instead of the customary one. I hastily put in the slot the penny that Mum had left on the kitchen table with one for the bottle of school milk. I turned the knob and hey presto, two packets of chewing-gum appeared. This cheered me up. The school bell started as we all hurried down Balaam Street to school. I'll stick to marbles in future, I thought.

It was Monday morning, and it was hymns and prayers for the first half hour. We formed up into our classes in the hall, the smaller ones in the front, taller boys at the back. Thankfully the taller of us thought that we were well beyond Old Tom Lethaby's watchful eye.

Our teachers, with their backs to the classrooms, stood as if to attention, waiting for the headmaster to come down from his study and take up his customary position at the side of the big shiny table. The clock above it said nine o'clock.

Just half an hour and our class would be crossing the playground, climbing the iron staircase and going into the classroom for a woodwork lesson. At the end of the benches was the rack of tools, just like the grown-ups used. I was making a medicine cabinet. During the last few weeks, I had cut the sides, top and bottom and the plywood back.

'Don't forget,' Mr Leithead said. 'Line on the left, saw on the right.' Woe betide anybody who ignored his advice. I liked woodwork.

'Daydreaming again, Kimberley,' Mr Murray called out. 'Pay attention and look to the front.'

A lady teacher from the girls' school, one floor below us, sat down at the upright piano, organising the sheet music in front of her. Mr Cronshaw rolled down from high up on the wall the first hymn we would sing, and laid his long pointer by it. Mr Murray glanced at his wristwatch.

'Good morning, boys.'

'Good morning, sir,' the school answered as Mr Lethaby strode up to the table and stood by it. He held up his hand. Complete silence reigned.

'I want you all this morning to sing the hymns as loudly as you can for me.' He nodded to Mr Cronshaw who in turn nodded to the piano player, picked up his long pointer and indicated the first line

of the first hymn. Keeping in time with the pianist, his pointer followed the line, hoping that we in turn would follow him. Some of us did, but a lot didn't. We did our best, but it wasn't to the headmaster's liking.

'Wait, wait, stop, stop!' he cried. 'You boys at the back, I can't hear you at all. Sing up, sing up.'

At a nod from Mr Cronshaw the piano lady tried again, and again, and again. So did 300 or so boys.

Short and tall, fat and thin, we tried to please. Mr Cronshaw's face became blacker and blacker, especially when Old Lethaby snatched his pointer and despairingly pointed to the first line of 'All Things Bright and Beautiful'

once again, on this not so bright Monday morning.

I saw Mr Murray quietly turn back his cuff and look high up into the ceiling of the hall. I too sneaked a look at the clock on the wall high above Mr Lethaby's table.

Crikey, look at the time! It was nearly ten o'clock. That's a whole half hour of our woodwork gone. I'll never get Mum's medicine cabinet done in time for her birthday at this rate!

The eleventh day of the eleventh month

'We're all to stand to attention, with feet together, hands by our sides.'

'Right, lads, you can pack up now.' We had waited for old Murray to say this, as he always did at a quarter to four on Friday afternoons. There was a noisy scramble as desk lids were raised and books, pencils and rulers were hastily put away until Monday morning.

'Not so much noise!' Raising his voice to be heard above the din he added, 'Don't forget the A team kicks off at 9am tomorrow and the B team at 10am. And don't be late.'

Pointing at Steppo he said, 'Don't forget your boots this week and make sure they have studs on them. Oh, and by the way, Stephens, what's special about tomorrow?'

Steppo shuffled to his feet. 'Er, well it's Saturday tomorrow, sir.'

Old Murray put on his best glare.

'Fathead. The infants school downstairs know it's Saturday tomorrow, Stephens. Barret, stand up and tell Stephens what's so special about tomorrow.'

Alf stood up and said with a know-all look, 'It's Poppy Day tomorrow, sir.'

To me, still with his glare on, old Murray said, 'Kimberley, clean the blackboard down!'

Mr Murray

'Kimberley, stay behind. I want a word with you.'

Crikey, I thought. What've I done now? As the class filed out, I murmured to Alf, 'See you in the park.'

I stood in front of Mr Murray's table. He finished marking an exercise book, and put it on a pile of others. He looked up and said, 'Kimberley, do you get enough to eat at home?'

'Er, er. . . Enough to eat?'

'Enough to eat.'

How could anyone think that our Mum didn't give us enough to eat! It came out in a rush. 'Course I do, sir, course I do. Our Mum's always telling us off for not eating all of our dinner up, and she's always telling me off, and says that I chase about too much.'

A bit of a smile came on his face as he said, 'Well, you're very tall for your age and being the school's football team's centre half I would like to see you grow out the other way' – he lifted his hands and spread them out – 'like this. So promise me you'll do as she says. Off you go then.'

'Blooming cheek,' I thought as I kicked the ball as hard as I could. Cor, Mum would be upset and cross if I told her. Not enough to eat! I'll tell Bob. No, better not, cos he'll come up to the school and tell old Murray off for sure. I never ever did tell anybody, and never ever did get fat!

The classes came and went – 1a, 2a, 3a, 4a – and over the years old Murray proved to be a good, kind, caring teacher. Strict but fair. The three Rs were the love of his life and he made sure they were ours too, although I admit somewhat grudgingly at times! Woe betide any one of us who fell below the standards he set!

Class 4a, and suddenly I was 14 years of age! I stood in front of his table and waited for him to write my school report.

'Good luck, lad,' he said as he handed it to me.

I put it on the kitchen table for Mum to read. He had written: 'Kenneth Kimberley has attended this school since 1929 and I have no hesitation in recommending him for a position in your company. I am sure he will given loyal and satisfactory service. In the subject of art he was outstanding. In arithmetic, writing and spelling he was above average. Signed, Leonard Murray, December 1939, Teacher.'

'He must have thought a lot of you,' Mum said.

Looking back, I am sure that all of us were grateful for his years of good guidance. The knowledge, the discipline and fairness he endeavoured to instil in us all helped us to face up to the war years that lay ahead; after all, at 14 we were still only his lads!

We all inwardly groaned as I hurried towards the front of the class and did as I was told. The chalk squeaked on the blackboard. Quarter to four was forgotten as old Murray wrote in large letters 'ON THE ELEVENTH HOUR.

'ON THE ELEVENTH DAY. OF THE ELEVENTH MONTH.'

He finished each line with a large dot and such a flourish that the chalk broke in pieces and fell to the floor. Shall I pick up the pieces, I wondered. At the back of the class, Charlie Mount whispered to Steppo.

'Tell 'im at 11 o'clock tomorrow, when the ships' sirens sound in the docks and Whitefield's factory hooter goes off, tell 'im we're all to stand to attention, with feet together, hands by our sides and not to move for two whole minutes!'

Mr Murray turned from the blackboard. 'I am waiting, Stephens. What have we all to do at 11am tomorrow?'

Steppo looked up at the ceiling and took a deep breath. We all held ours, as he told us all what was expected of us, and added, 'Oh, and I am playing for the B team against St Luke's in the morning and after that I am going to the pictures to see Laurel & Hardy, sir!'

The bandstand

We looked up at the noticeboard by the park gate. Charlie Mount read it aloud: 'The Enfield and District Silver and Brass Band will play in the bandstand on each Wednesday during July from 7.30-9.30pm. Deckchairs 3d and 6d.'

'That's tomorrow,' we all exclaimed.

We arrived early and made ourselves comfortable on the railings that surrounded the bandstand, watching as the mums and grans in their summer dresses, dads and grandads in the Sunday best, got their tickets from old Parky and sat down in their deckchairs. Perched on the railings we had a grandstand view of all the comings and goings.

'Look over there. That's Alfie Cockerton's mum and dad, and Mr and Mrs Golding!'

The deckchairs quickly became occupied, as we busied ourselves pointing out every known new arrival.

'Here comes the band,' Alf said, as the smart uniformed bandsmen made their way down the pathway to the bandstand, carrying their gleaming trumpets, bugles and drums.

'Cor, they look like the Salvation Army,' exclaimed Albie.

'Oh don't be daft,' replied Charlie. 'They come from Enfield and that's a posh place.'

A hush settled – you could hear a pin drop as the conductor raised his arm and tapped his baton on the music stand.

We all held our breath, waiting for the big moment. It came, and we joined in with the mums and dads singing 'My old man said follow the van, And don't dilly-dally on the way. . .' We joined in with 'Sing as we go, and let the world go by', and 'Say goodbye to sorrow, think of tomorrow, and not of today'.

Finally, the bandmaster held his baton aloft. 'Thank you for joining in with us, ladies and gentlemen. There will now be a short interval to enable you to get your breath

A notice-board reads 'NO BALL GAMES TO BE PLAYED HERE' – Parky would have loved that! It's greener today than I remember, being all grassed over. I still recognise some of the trees, especially the one with a seat round it – it was Grandad's favourite. The ornate bandstand where locals were entertained on fine sunny days is gone, and the ornamental pond with its fountain and the flower garden are mere shadows of their long-ago glory.

back!' (Much laughter and clapping) 'After a short interlude we will play for you a selection of popular ballads.'

'What's a ballad?' asked Albie.

Know-all Charlie said, 'It's a quiet sort of song. Just shut up and listen.'

As the sun disappeared behind the rooftops in Balaam Street coloured lights lit up the bandstand and shone on the hanging-baskets full of trailing flowers and the banks of flowers that surrounded it. Some reflected up into the glossy, green leaves of the trees around us.

'Oi, you lot, off the railings.' We all inwardly groaned; we knew it was old Parky that had come up behind us. Having done his duty selling deckchair tickets he was now looking for other things to do. We grudgingly got down from the railings.

'Oh all right. We don't want to listen to your old band anyway,' said Albie.

'Cheeky whippersnapper – 'op it!'

We trooped out of the park and dejectedly kicked a tennis ball between ourselves down Balaam Street. Over the roofs and treetops we could hear them singing

'Roamin' in the gloamin' wi' a lassie by my side'.

Alf walked up the path to his front door. Mrs Barret was sitting at her upstairs window enjoying the last moments of the summer's day and the music that came over the rooftops.

The whopper

'It's the biggest tiddler we've ever caught!'

It was a sunny morning as we made our way down Prince Regent Lane. We passed the secondary school. ('That's where you go if you pass your scholarship,' said know-all Charlie.) Over his shoulder Albie Gibbs carried the 'dragging sack', Eddy carried one of his mum's buckets, and the rest of us were armed with the usual collection of fishing nets and jam-jars.

We scrambled over a rickety fence on to the soft boggy fields that seemed to stretch out for ever before us.

In the far distance ships' funnels and masts poked over the rooftops of Custom House and Woolwich beyond. Not too far away was the soap factory, and as we found a grassy mound amongst the narrow shallow streams that criss-crossed the area, a big puff of dirty yellow smoke came out of the tall, spindly chimney that rose from the factory's corrugated roof. It wasn't long before we were all holding our noses.

However, we quickly forgot the smell as we made ourselves comfortable and laid out our bits and pieces. Off came our shoes and socks and we waded into the shallow stream. The water barely covered our ankles and the bottom was all soft and squelchy as we paddled about. Albie took one end of the sack, Eddy the other. I scooped enough of the murky water to half fill the bucket. They gently lowered the sack into the water and dragged it along the bottom. After a few minutes they brought it to the surface. They tipped the murky water out and with it a few tiddlers. Charlie and Alf turned up their noses. Charlie said, 'I'm going to try another spot.'

'Gee whiz, look at those!' we exclaimed, as we spotted them darting and waving about as the sun penetrated the dark water and gleamed on their tiny backs. 'I'll run and tell them to bring the drag up here,' I said.

Minutes later Albie and Eddy were in the water dragging away. They scooped up a lot of

Charlie Mount

We all envied Charlie. At the end of a long day in the park, when old Parky rang the bell before locking the gates, Charlie could nip through bushes, bunk up over the fence and into his own back yard. His long legs ensured that he was up and over in a flash, before old Parky could bat an eyelid! And if he wanted, in the summer time he could sit at his bedroom window and listen to the band, and watch all the goings on!

At heart I believe he preferred nuts and bolts, soap boxes and pram wheels to the mundane street games we played. You did your best to keep out of Charlie's team at Oi Jimmy Knacker, as his long legs invariably meant that his feet touched the ground before we even got started!

Sitting in style in his latest box on wheels, with his legs stretched out before him, his hands firmly gripping the string that guided this latest masterpiece, he would whiz up and down the street, never being short of somebody to do the pushing.

However, Charlie was first and foremost a Scout. Nobody could pitch a tent on Wanstead Flats like Charlie – an old sheet, a few sticks, some string and a few other bits and pieces and hey presto we had a cool retreat to drink our fizzy lemonade on those long hot summer days!

When we went our separate ways during the war years, Charlie travelled to distant parts with the Merchant Navy, becoming a 3rd Engineer and finally coming ashore in 1952. He became a service engineer with a company in North London, and was asked to set up a subsidiary company in South Australia. He and Sheila set off for Melbourne, and they have been 'down under' ever since.

Charlie retired in 1989 as Chairman of two companies in Sydney and Melbourne. They now live on the sunshine coast in Western Australia, a long way from Balaam Street, his old soap boxes, and his pram wheels!

Becton's wide open spaces have vanished under bricks and tarmac, and it all smells a bit sweeter than it did! Close by is the McMillan sports complex offering rugby, soccer and running tracks, all floodlit, as well as a superb indoor swimming-pool and cafeteria. I wonder where the Balaam Street boys do their tiddler fishing these days!

sticklebacks and emptied them into the half-filled bucket as we gathered round and gazed at our catch. I tipped a packet of lemonade powder into the milk bottle and gave it a good shake, and we crunched away on the broken biscuits and sat back, pleased with ourselves.

The horses on their long tethers ventured as far as they could towards us. The gypsy children looked to be playing hide and seek under the caravan, their dogs chasing about with them. Occasionally they stopped and stared at us, wondering, I expect, what we intruders were up to.

'Cor, what a whopper,' I said, as I admired the big stickleback in the jam-jar. 'It's the biggest tiddler we've ever caught.'

'There's something on my foot!' shouted Eddy, hobbling out of the water on one leg. Albie pulled out the drag and emptied the remains of a broken milk bottle on to the grass. Eddy hopped around on one leg, looking down at his bleeding foot. Charlie Mount took charge. He was a Cub or Scout, I forget which.

'Gotta stop it bleeding,' he said with authority. 'Anybody got a handkerchief?' I delved in my pocket and found amongst the odd bits of string a marble that I

thought I had lost, and a none-too-clean handkerchief – Mum would have a fit if she knew I had that in my pocket, I thought.

'Sit down, Eddy,' said Charlie, and proceeded to bind up his big toe with my grubby handkerchief.

'Suppose we'd better go home now.' We looked at Eddy as if to imply that he had brought our day to an early close.

'I can't get my shoe on,' he wailed.

By now Charlie was in complete charge. 'We'll have to give him a piggy-back ride home. We can take it in turns. Take off your other shoe, Ed.' He tied them together and hung them round Eddy's neck.

An hour later, after a lot of huffing and puffing, we left Eddy on his mother's doorstep, knocked on the knocker and scarpered; we didn't want to listen to the wrath of Mrs Gill when she saw Eddy's bleeding toe and my grubby handkerchief!

Christmas

We looked into the wonderland of fairy-lights and Christmas trees.

'Gee whiz, I'd like those soldiers and the fort to go with them.'

'No, I'd sooner have that racing car.'

With our noses pressed against the glass, each one of us stated our preference for our hoped-for Christmas present, as we looked into the wonderland of fairy lights, Christmas trees, paper chains and lanterns. The more we looked the greater our excitement became. Above the ohs and ahs I asked Steppo what he hoped to have for Christmas.

'Er, well. . .' Steppo looked down at the pavement and seemed reluctant to answer.

'Come on,' I said. 'There must be something you hope you're going to get.'

Still looking at the pavement, he said, 'Er, me dad's out of work, so I don't expect me and me sister will get anything this Christmas.' With that he left us and joined Albie who was warming himself at the hot chestnut stand by old Ponder's vegetable stall.

Alf, hearing Steppo's sad news, said, 'There's still seven days to Christmas,' carefully counting each day off on his fingers. 'I know, we'll go carol singing. What we get we'll spend on a Christmas present for Steppo and his sister.'

'I can't sing very well,' somebody said.

'Oh that doesn't matter so long as we make a noise. Come on, we'll start tonight.'

Pleased with ourselves and Alf's bright idea, we set off for home, singing 'Good King Wenceslas'. As we went the barrel-organ joined in with us.

'We're knocking at your knocker, ringing at your bell. Please spare a copper for singing up so well.'

We ended our carol as the Salvation Army ended theirs – we couldn't have been more lucky. They struck up 'Good King Wenceslas' and we hurriedly joined in, at a distance, with our vocal support.

The harmonious noise we made between us gave us the confidence to knock at old Chambers's front door.

'Knock then,' we said to Albie, as we nudged him up the doorstep. Moments later a light came on in the fanlight above the door. As Mr

Chambers stood on the step, his cat as always sat beside him, the warmth from the passageway flooded out over us.

''ere you are, lads,' he said. 'There's tuppence to go and sing down the next street.'

'Cor, thanks, Mr Chambers,' we all said, and wished him a Happy Christmas.

Our band had moved further down the street.

'Quick, let's chase after them.'

We knew we were on to a good thing, and we joined in with them as they struck up 'While shepherds watched their flocks by night'. When we reached the bottom of the street they all came over to us, and said, laughing, 'Have you done all right this evening, lads?'

'Cor, yes, we 'ave,' we replied, as we each felt for the coppers that were lining our pockets.

One of the musicians said, 'We're up on the Broadway tomorrow evening. Meet us up there. Who knows, you might do even better. Goodnight, and God bless you.'

We hurried back up the street, unable to believe our luck.

Snowballs

'Wake up, lazybones,' I heard Bob say. 'Come on, you'll be late for school.'

With this he pulled the bedclothes back, adding, 'You know that Mum likes you to be up before she goes off to work.'

'Oh all right,' I grumbled.

I tiptoed across the cold lino to where my clothes were on the chair, and hurriedly scrambled into them, pausing at the window to look and see a white blanket over everything.

'Gee whiz,' I thought. 'It must be three inches deep.'

I hurried downstairs. The kitchen was warm and cosy, the fire in the range burning brightly. Mum always banked it up last thing at night, and we did the same when we left for school; it was hardly ever out in the winter. Bob was kneeling in front of the grate with a piece of bread on the end of a toasting fork. On the hearth by his side was a plate with more pieces. I went into the kitchen. Mum was at the gas stove, stirring the porridge.

'There's hot water in the kettle,' she said, 'enough for you to wash in – and don't forget to clean your teeth.'

I emptied the kettle into the enamel bowl, placed it in the sink, tucked my collar into my shirt and washed.

Mum brought our porridge in to us as we sat at the kitchen table. 'Eat it all up,' she said. We did, and Bob's toast too.

'I'll get your overcoats out of the wardrobe. Your boots are in the cupboard under the stairs, and don't forget your scarves and caps. It looks as if the sky is full of snow today.'

Mum hurried upstairs, coming down moments later with her hat and coat on, and her bag under her arm.

'I'm off now.' Bob went up the passage with her and I heard her say to him, 'Make sure Ken puts his overcoat on, and his boots, and his cap and scarf, and you too, don't forget. And don't forget to put the guard up in front of the fire and turn the damper down. Oh, and make sure you close the front door when you go to school.'

'Yes, Mum,' I heard Bob say, adding, 'Mind how you go in the snow, Mum.'

He came back into the kitchen. We finished our breakfast together then took the plates and things into the scullery and washed them up. Bob made up the fire and closed the damper, and I put the fire guard in place on the hearth. We struggled into our boots and overcoats.

'Where's your cap and scarf?' asked Bob.

'Oh, do I have to?'

'Yes you do – just do as you're told for once and put them on.'

I looked at Grandad's clock on the mantelpiece. It was a quarter to nine.

'Come on, Ken, or we'll be late.'

Bob closed the front door with a bang and gave it a good pull to see that it was closed. He held my arm and said, 'Look after yourself and don't be late home from school.'

Then he went off to Plaistow Sec and I went off to Balaam Street. We turned and waved to each other as we went our separate ways.

Charlie Mount, with whom I shared a desk, whispered, 'It's snowing again.'

We were having a geography lesson. Like everyone else, I was endeavouring to draw in my exercise book a map of Africa, doing my best to remember where the Sahara Desert was before colouring it in with my yellow pencil. At Charlie's insistence I looked out of the classroom window, across to the tram sheds, thinking, 'I bet they don't have snow in Africa!' Five minutes later, having decided where to put the Sahara Desert on my map, Charlie whispered again.

'It's stopped.'

I looked up again. There was now a clear blue sky over the roofs of the tram sheds.

'Not so much talking at the back of the class. I won't tell you again,' Mr Murray called out. We lowered our heads and thought of sunny Africa.

As we left school at four o'clock the snowball fights began. They carried on down Barber's Alley, along Balaam Street and into the park. The park looked like a Christmas card, especially as the

sun was going down over the rooftops and making the snow-covered branches on the trees glisten. It was a white wonderland that hadn't seen a footprint all day, except for old Parky's big

wellingtons. We spotted him between the tall trees that lined the pathway, and stopped our own feuding, intent on giving Parky what for.

On the round seat beneath the tree by the bandstand we quickly made our pile of snowballs, then hid ourselves behind the trees. As Parky came up the path into range we let him have it. We each had a score to settle.

'That one's for keeping us off the grass!'

'That one's for telling us to 'op it!'

'That one's for chasing us out of the bushes!'

'That one's for not letting us sit on your old railings!'

As the snowballs rained down, old Parky called out, 'I'll be up to see your headmaster in the morning!'

Sweet revenge

'Oi mister, you can't leave that there – it's our football pitch!'

'Oi you can't leave that there,' we called out. Jimmy Cox looked at us as he got out of his big black motor car.

'Can't leave it here?' he said. 'I'll leave my car where I like – and if that there ball of yours as much as comes near my car I'll kick it over the roof-tops.'

With that he slammed the door, locked it and went into the house.

Jimmy Cox was a grown-up none of us liked. His mum and dad owned the empty shop up the street, next door to the big stable that Jimmy ran his taxi business from. He lived with his sister opposite our house, and more often than not left his car, the only one in

the street, parked outside, and of course it was in the way of our street games.

As we came home from school one day, the big wooden doors of the stable were thrown wide open. The pavement outside and the top of his car were piled high with suitcases and trunks of all shapes and sizes. I paused and peered at the numerous labels that were stuck on the trunks amidst the chalk 'NOT WANTED ON VOYAGE' scribbles. One read 'Major S. Harvey, The Essex Regt, Warley Barracks, Essex, Eng'. There were so many – it was difficult to see some trunks for all the labels stuck on them! P&O Line, Bibby Line, White Star Line – some were half scratched off and replaced with newer ones.

Another read: 'Captn C. E. Bell R. Navy Retd, Fwd to Rose Cottage, The Street, Melton, Dorset, Eng. En route from RN Establishment, Trincomalee, Ceylon.'

I was fascinated just looking at the labels on the battered and bruised trunks and cases. As I wandered idly about them, I conjured up pictures of faraway places that we could only read of in the geography books at school. Not realising that I was now deep inside the stable, in the gloom I saw bearded sea captains and wax-moustached majors. I could see Mr J. C. David Shrubshaw bound for his tea plantation in faraway India. All these pictures I could see were,

for the time being, stored right here in Khartoum Road, E13.

'What are you doing in here?' Jimmy stormed. 'This is private property.'

'I was only looking,' I muttered.

'You go and look somewhere else,' he shouted.

Jimmy Cox must have mislaid one of his trunks, I thought as I hurried out into the bright sunshine, or perhaps one of the labels has come off one of his cases. ''ope he don't find it.'

We all sat dejected on the railings outside the corner shop with nothing do to. We all agreed that Jimmy Cox was an old misery and wanted taking down a peg or two. It was then that we laid our plans for our sweet revenge.

'Have you got the matchsticks, Ken?' Charlie asked me.

We were gathered under the lamp-post by the sewer wall. I fumbled in my pocket and found the matchsticks that I had taken from the full box on the gas stove in the scullery.

'It's still there,' Alf said as we innocently looked down the darkened street at Jimmy Cox's big black car. Thankfully not too much light spilled out from parlour windows and passage fanlights as we crept towards the car. We knelt down by the front wheel, the one farthest away from old Cox's front door.

'Sh! Don't make any noise,' Alf said. 'I'll take the dust-cap off.'

Charlie straight away pushed a matchstick into the inner-tube valve that was poking up through the spokes of the wheel.

'Oh,' he said, 'the matchstick's broke.'

I fiddled around in my pocket

and found the others, but dropped them in my haste to give one to Charlie. On my knees I found one and handed it to him. There was a loud hissing noise as the matchstick found the valve. In the half dark we watched, all on our knees now, as

the tyre slowly flattened. Alfie hurriedly screwed the dust cap back in place. We scarpered!

Next day in the school playground we decided to do it again that night. After dark we crept up to the car again. I bent down.

'Cor,' I said, 'it's a job to get the dust-cap off.'

'Let me do it,' said Alf.

As I stood up, Jimmy Cox's parlour window lit up, as did the fanlight over the front door. With that the door flew open!

'Gotcha!' he called out, as he leapt over the doorstep. 'I'll have your guts for garters when I get hold of you.'

We gave him little chance, as we chased off down the street as fast as our legs would carry us!

The swimming-baths

'Stephens, I hope you've got your costume this week!'

'Mum, do you know where my swimming costume is?'

'Where it always is,' she replied. On the copper in the scullery, rolled up in a clean towel.'

She went up the passage and put on her hat and coat. Picking up her bag she went to the street door, then turned and said, 'Don't forget to dry yourself properly and mind you dry your hair well. Give it a good rub when you come out.'

Then she went off to catch the bus up at the top.

Bob came into the scullery. 'Have you learned to swim yet, cos it's about time?'

'I know,' I replied, 'but when I take my feet off the bottom I just go under.'

'Oh, you're just scared, that's the trouble with you,' he said.

Later, as I walked to school with my towel under my arm and my costume wrapped up inside it, I thought, 'I'll show him!'

The ornate disinfectant-smelling building where we learned to swim is no more, and on the site stands the Newham Leisure Centre. There are no fears about learning today in this super swimming pool at the McMillan Centre, Prince Regents Lane.

Class 3a lined up in the playground.

'Right,' said Mr Emmet. 'Have you all got your swimming costumes and towels?'

'Yes, sir,' we answered.

'Off we go then,' he said, 'and no skylarking about at the back.'

We all filed out of the gate, down Barber's Alley and along Balaam Street to the baths. Of course there was skylarking about at the back.

'If there's any more of it we'll turn round and go straight back to school and have an arithmetic lesson for the rest of the morning!'

With this threat hanging over us there was no more skylarking about. As we passed the scrap iron yard I could just see the tea and coffee stall over the wall. When it got dark it was pushed out into the street by the grown-ups, one between the shafts pulling, the other at the back pushing.

On arrival, Mr Emmet stood at the top of the stone steps beneath the big arched opening. As Steppo went through the door, he said, 'I hope you've remembered to bring your swimming costume today, Stephens.'

We filed into the second-class bath, which was on the right-hand side of the entrance hall. The first-class bath was on the left-hand side and was a much posher place: it was bigger and had a balcony all round with seats.

I hated the carbolicky smell of it all. Even on a hot summer's day it seemed cold and grey. Every word seemed to echo round and round the tiled walls. I hung my clothes behind the door in the tiny cubicle and struggled into my costume. We heard Mr Emmet's whistle. There was a scramble to get lined up on the edge of the swimming-pool. He was already standing in the water.

'When I blow the whistle once,' he said, 'I want the boys on my left to jump in and endeavour to swim to the other side. As he put the whistle to his mouth he spotted poor old Steppo behind the door.

'Stephens!' he shouted. 'What are you doing behind there, and where's your costume?'

We forgot Steppo as he blew his whistle. As one and with a big splash, we jumped into the shallow end of the bath. As my feet touched the tiled bottom my knees bent

beneath me and I got a mouthful and eyeful of the carbolic-tasting water. There was bedlam all around

as we tried to get across to the other side. As I struck out with flailing arms, my feet, as if

somebody was holding them up, came off the bottom and I was afloat! I couldn't believe it, and

moments later, with a few others, I reached the other side. I scrambled out but in a few moments jumped

back in again, just to make sure that I could swim, really swim at last.

I gave my head a last good rub with the towel.

'Get fell in, lads,' said Mr Emmet; turning to Steppo he added, 'I'll talk to you later back at school. And no skylarking about on the way back.'

'Poor old Steppo,' I thought. 'He always cops it.'

When I got home I poked my head round the parlour door, where I knew Bob would be doing his homework.

'I did it,' I said.

'Did what?' he asked.

'I can swim, so I wasn't scared, was I?'

'Don't be daft. I was only teasing you.'

Ernie Bright

We felt sorry for Ernie. He sat in the front row of the class, right under old Murray's nose. He sat there because he wore glasses, so he could see the blackboard!

Being tall I sat in the back row, as did Charlie Mount, with whom I shared a desk. As we sat right up the back of the class, it was left to Ernie and his fellow occupants on the front row to fall foul of old Murray's glare and Monday morning moods!

'Silence!' old Murray called. 'Here are the summer term's examination results. Top of the class is E. Bright, second is K. Kimberley.'

Ernie turned round from his desk at the front and gave me a big grin.

Mr Murray droned on with the results of our endeavours of the last few months. We all knew who would be bottom – poor old Steppo.

When we talk of those days today, Ernie and I have a laugh, because over the years when he came top, I came second, or if I was top he claimed the second place, and that was how it was in our schooldays at Balaam Street. However, when we reached the summit, class 4a, I had the last laugh, because I was made school captain. Ernie, you've guessed it, became vice-captain!

The war and evacuation came and we lost touch, although not for long. Going about my daily rounds in my first office job in the city, who should I bump into in the office on the floor below but Ernie B!

Ernie came back into the fold, joining the old Balaam Street boys in our football and bike trips and the rest of it. The early 1940s rushed past us. War or no war we all enjoyed ourselves, but then came the day when we had to choose either the Army, Navy or Air Force. Ernie chose the Army. After training at Catterick Camp, Yorkshire, he served in the Middle East as a wireless operator, and came back to civvy street in 1947.

The Balaam Street boys picked up the threads once again and we were all soon off again on our bikes, football in the park on Sunday mornings and, of course, cheering on the Hammers on Saturday afternoons!

Time flies and Ernie retired in 1987 from his job as a national sales manager with a UK food company. A family man, with children and grandchildren, he still enjoys golf and squash and gardening. How does he do it? I wish I knew!

'Keep it up, Bright, keep it up!' I can almost hear old Murray saying! I hope he can, too, for many years to come.

Then all quiet, as if somebody was listening at the parlour window, he said, 'If you want to learn to swim really properly like me and Johnny Sullivan did, go to the YMCA in Greengate Street. There's a smashing swimming-bath in the basement there -but don't tell everybody, will you?'

'But I don't belong to the YMCA. But nor do you, do you?'

'Oh, that doesn't matter,' he replied. 'Johnny found that there's a side door that leads to the basement where the swimming-bath is. It's never locked cos it's an emergency exit. Go down the side of the YMCA and it's at the bottom of some steps. If you go down there after school like Johnny and me did nobody will ever see you.'

'But what if they do?' I asked, sounding worried.

'Oh, they can only chuck you out,' he replied.

A week later my pal Ernie Bright and me found the door that Bob said was always open. We looked

From the outside the fine YMCA building is unaltered, but it is now part of the University of East London – is there still a swimming-pool in the basement, I wonder?

about us, sneaked down the alleyway by the YMCA, pushed open the door and there at the bottom of the stairs was the swimming-pool. It was quiet and deserted. If it hadn't been we would have turned on our heels and

scarpered. We tiptoed into a cubicle, changed into our costumes and in a few moments we were in the water. It didn't taste or smell a bit like the second-class swimming-bath down Balaam Street. It was smashing! I managed to get from one side to the other, and before we left, with Ernie's encouragement because he was better at swimming than me, I swam a whole length of the bath.

Some weeks later, walking down to the YMCA, confident now that we wouldn't be found out, Ernie said, 'I've worked it out, Ken. If we swim up and down the bath ten times we will have swum over a quarter of a mile.'

'Honest?' I said. 'Gosh, let's have a go.'

Later we tiptoed back up the stairs to the door and went out into the bright sunshine, as pleased as Punch that we could swim a whole quarter of a mile. I couldn't get home quick enough to tell Bob!

The school holiday camp

I walked slowly through the park and up to the school. Since it was only 8 o'clock in the morning it was quiet and deserted. Mum and Bob waved goodbye at our gate.

'Here's your suitcase,' said Mum. 'Make sure you don't lose the key, and look after your pocket-money.'

For as I long as I could remember she had been giving me sixpence every Monday to give to Mr Murray towards the school holiday camp fund. Four of us were going from our class to start with, but three had dropped out. That left me as the only one going from Class 3a to the camp at St Helens on the Isle of Wight that morning in late August.

I saw Mr Solly and Mr Emmet in the playground with boys from other schools whom I had never seen before. Already I was missing my own school pals as we climbed on to the charabanc that took us to a station in London.

'Now, boys, line up here.' Mr Solly and Mr Emmet between them sorted us into some sort of order.

I had never been into a real dockyard before and the only ships I had seen were the ones at the swing-bridge where Grandad used to take us, and of course when I went toing and froing on the Woolwich Free Ferry with my pals. But here at Portsmouth we eagerly queued up to go up the gangway to HMS *Victory*, the most famous ship of all.

'Mind you behave yourselves,' Mr Solly said as he stood at the foot of the gangway. Mr Emmet had led the way and we all followed hard on his heels.

'I am Chief Petty Officer Trevello. This here is my colleague Petty Officer Symes. We will split into two parties. The petty officer will escort one party and I the other.'

'Right, lads, get into two groups,' Mr Solly hastily said.   We did as he asked. We were all eyes as the petty officer, in his smart uniform and peaked cap, escorted us along the wooden deck, pausing for a moment to say, 'The *Victory* was laid down at Chatham in May 1765 and Admiral Nelson raised his flag on the *Victory* on 18 May 1805.' As he talked we stared up in wonderment at the tall masts and the maze of ropes, and the scrubbed woodwork, the like of which we had never seen before.

'Gee whiz,' I thought. 'The old ferry down at Woolwich was never anything like this.'

'If you will follow me, lads. . .' We quickly fell in behind him as he led the way up and down ladders. 'This here is the poop deck, and this is the upper deck.' We stared up at the main mast that seemed to go up and up for ever. He showed us round the lower deck, the powder store and the magazine. We looked in awe at the cannons, and our guide explained the different rope tackles for loading and unloading them. We stopped up on the quarter deck.

'Well, lads,' said the petty officer, 'if you know your history lessons you will know that Admiral Nelson was shot in the spine and was mortally wondered at the Battle of Trafalgar on 21 October 1805. You there, lad' – pointing at me – 'you're standing on the very same spot.'

I hastily jumped aside and we all looked down in silence to where I had been standing.

'Follow me, lads,' and we were off again to Nelson's cabin. 'This is where he knelt down and said his last prayer.' Taking a little book from his pocket, he opened it and read to us. '"May the God I worship grant to my country a great and glorious victory. I commit my life to Him who made me, and may His blessing light on my endeavours for serving my country faithfully. Amen." Moments later he joined the captain on the quarter deck and requested that a signal should be made. It read "That on this day England expects that every man will do his duty". Follow me, lads.'

We stopped again at his request deep down in the *Victory*. 'This is where a sergeant in the marines carried and laid him down. Admiral Nelson said, "They have done for me at last", but he heard from Thomas Hardy's lips, his captain and dear friend, that he had achieved a glorious victory that he had prayed for, before dying on this very spot.'

It was late in the afternoon when we arrived at St Helens.

'We're too late for tea, lads, but supper won't be too long,' Mr Solly announced. We struggled across the field with our belongings.

'That's the cookhouse, that's the wash-house, and the big tent is where we have our meals,' he said.

The large bell tents were lined up in a row against a tall hedge.

'Four of you in a tent,' he said. He ushered the first four of us inside. After the heat of the long day it was cool and inviting. I had never been in a proper tent before, except what Charlie Mount called a tent in our days out on Wanstead Flats. Four palliasses were spaced evenly around the edge pointing towards the tent poles, with two blankets and a pillow neatly laid on each.

'Put your cases and bags at the foot of your palliasse.' Taking mine from me, he said, 'Like this, cos we want to keep everything tidy and shipshape, don't we?' He then left us to it and went down the line of tents, shepherding four boys into each.

An hour later, as the long summer day came to a close, Mr Solly and Mr Emmet called in at each tent, wishing us goodnight and to sleep well. I pulled the blankets up over me and recalled the excitement of the day. As I lay there I thought of Mum and Bob for the first time since waving goodbye to them at the gate. I pulled the blankets further up and was soon sound asleep.

After breakfast in the big tent Mr Solly told us all to go to the cookhouse and get our packed lunches because a charabanc would be taking us to Alum Bay. The charabanc was waiting for us in the lane outside the camp. We climbed aboard, each one dashing to get a seat by the window, settled down, then turned our attention to the contents of the lunch bags.

'I've got a corned beef sandwich. I'll swap you for my cheese one,' and so it went on for five minutes until Mr Solly and Mr Emmet sat in the front seats by the driver. With the sandwich was a Milky Way, an apple and a big bag of Smiths crisps.

The lunch bags were quickly forgotten as the chara sped along the highways and byways of the island. It was all so green. It stopped on a grassy verge, and through the trees we could see a big house.

'That's Osborne House, lads,' Mr Solly said. 'That's where Queen Victoria lived. It was built in 1845. She died there in 1901.' The charabanc sped off again. Mr Solly turned round in his seat. 'I hope you are all remembering what you have seen, because between tea time and supper time this evening I want you all to write in your exercise books and tell me what you can remember of these last two days.'

A cheeky voice said at the back of the chara, 'I thought we were on holiday, sir.'

Mr Solly and Mr Emmet looked at each other and laughed aloud.

'Here we are, boys. Off we all get.'

Mr Emmet had told us on the way to Alum Bay that it was famous for its coloured sands, and he was sure that we would wish to take some home, explaining that in the gift shop in the village we could buy tiny glass tubes that we could fill with layers of the sand; with a cork in the top we would have a souvenir to take back home. We walked in an orderly line along the cliff top.

Mr Emmet pointed to the sea. 'That's the English Channel, lads, and 50 miles away is France.'

'Cor,' we exclaimed. 'Have you ever been there, sir?'

'Yes,' he said. 'Matter of fact I have. Only a fortnight ago, cycling tour, on a tandem, you know, with my wife. Ah, and down there you can see the Needles.'

He pointed to the rocks that jutted out from the sea like fingers. It seemed that Mr Solly and Mr Emmet knew just about everything.

We all carefully descended the steps down to the pebbly beach, and had an exciting time scratching away and filling our glass tubes with the coloured sands. I filled one for Mum and one for my Aunt Liz. On each one there was a label that read 'A gift from Alum Bay'. Pleased with myself, I wrapped them carefully in my handkerchief and put them deep down in my shorts pocket.

'Come on, lads, time to get back on the coach and back to camp,' called Mr Solly.

On the way back the charabanc stopped with a jerk and the driver turned to Mr Solly. 'Do your boys wish to the see the *Queen Mary*, cos there she is, way out there,' and he pointed through the window to the large ship just visible in the haze on the horizon. 'Cherbourg first stop, then she's off to New York as fast as she can go.'

'Come on, lads, out you get if you want to see her.'

We needed no second asking – we had only seen her picture in the papers, never dreaming that we would see her in real life! We ran across the grassy verge. Mr Solly was looking through his binoculars.

'Please, sir, is that really her, the *Queen Mary*?'

'Yes,' he answered. 'I am certain it is. And that's something to write about in your exercise books when we get back to camp.'

Between tea time and supper time, for a change each tent and the field was quiet as we were all busy writing. I wrote as much as I could remember of the *Victory*, our ride to Alum Bay and the coloured sands, and seeing the *Queen Mary* on her way to New York. Later I took Mum and Aunt Liz's presents from my pocket and put them under my pillow.

'Everything all right, lads?' Mr Emmet asked us. 'You four are cooks today, I believe.'

'Yes, sir, that's right, sir.'

We waited for everyone to finish their breakfast, and as the last boy left the tent we gathered up the empty plates, knives and forks and tea mugs. It wasn't that we were real cooks, just that it was our turn today to take the dirty dishes back to the cookhouse, sweep under the long, wooden table and wipe the tables and benches down so that they were all clean and ready for the next meal.

'Make a good job of it,' he said, as he left us to it in the empty tent.

We stacked up the empty plates

on the iron trolley that we pushed up to the table, then Jimmy and me pushed it up the bumpy path to the scullery behind the cookhouse. We left our two tent-mates busy lifting the benches up on to the long table before sweeping the floor underneath. Jimmy knocked on the scullery door. A 'real' cook opened it, saying, 'Right-o, lads, leave it there. I'll empty it. You want your fanny of hot water, do you?'

'Yes please,' we replied. He disappeared into the scullery, reappearing moments later with the fanny, saying as he handed it to us, 'Be careful, lads, the water's very hot.'

Jimmy gripped one side of the handle, me the other. I never knew what happened next, just that I was lying on the path with Jimmy looking down at me. I yelled out as the hot water poured down my right leg. I wasn't wearing socks, just plimsolls, and I could feel the water run down my leg into them. Jimmy, untouched by the hot water, dashed off back to the cookhouse, appearing moments later with the two cooks. Between them they lifted me up and carried me through the scullery into the kitchen.

'Take his shoes off,' I heard one of them say, before dropping me feet-first into a barrel of something or other. 'The flour will take the pain away. It won't stop the blisters coming though.'

I didn't know whether to laugh or cry, being held up by the two cooks in a big barrel of flour! The horrible pain that I first felt down my legs was slowly easing.

'You all right, lad?' they asked.
'Yes thanks,' I mumbled.

One of them turned to Jimmy as he hovered about nearby. 'Pop across to your master's tent and tell him to come across, will you?' Jimmy dashed off. 'We're going to lift you out now, lad, and sit you on that stool. All right?'

As easily as they put me in the barrel they just as easily lifted me out, and sat me on the stool. Moments later old Solly hurried in, followed by Mr Emmet. The cook explained what had happened.

'Seems they tripped up with the fanny of hot water, sir,' he said.

'You all right, lad?' asked Mr Solly. 'Goodness me, just look at those blisters,' as they started to appear down my left leg and on to my foot.

'Funnily enough,' I thought, 'it doesn't hurt so much now.' Mr Solly turned to Mr Emmet. 'Dicky, nip up to the house and ask them to phone to get the doctor up here from the village, will you?' Turning to the cook he said, 'Be a good chap and help get him up on my back and I'll piggy-back him across to my tent.'

'Of course, sir. I'll come and give you a hand.'

On arrival they lowered me down on to Old Solly's deckchair. I heard the doctor say to him, 'Oh, he'll be all right by the end of the week. Not much I can do really. Those blisters will soon dry up. Make sure he keeps that leg dry and keep him out of water, whatever you do.'

I sat high up on the beach. Mr Emmet had given me a piggy-back down the short country lane, and I could only sit and watch as they all skylarked about on the beach below and in the water. I watched Mr Solly as he did a belly-flop into the surf as it came up the beach. Moments later he reappeared.

'That don't look like old Solly,' I thought. 'Crikey, where's his glasses?' I had never seen him without them before. He stumbled out of the surf and I watched as he went down on his hands and knees searching about for his glasses. I wished I could go and help as he groped about.

'Gosh,' I thought, 'he can hardly see.'

'Dicky!' I heard him shout. 'Come and help me find my glasses, will you?' Mr Emmet left the crowd of boys to their game of rounders further along the beach. The surf kept sweeping in and sweeping out. Mr Emmet said, 'The tide's going out, and I think it'll take your glasses with it, old man.'

'I'll have to send a wire home for the wife and ask her to send my spare pair,' said a disconsolate old Solly.

As we sat on the charabanc on the way to the ferry at the end of the week, Mr Solly stood up, now wearing his spare pair of glasses.

'Well, boys, Mr Emmet and I wish to thank you all for being so well behaved and hope you have enjoyed your week here at St Helens. We have enjoyed being here with you all.'

That evening, as I walked down Balaam Street, the skin on my leg still felt a bit stiff, but thankfully the blisters had all gone. I was pleased because I wouldn't have to tell Mum anything about it. As I neared home I felt in my pocket, just to make sure once again that the presents for her and Aunt Liz were still safely there.

Waiting for the balloon to go up

'Oi Postie, do you want to borrow our Billy's pop-gun?'

'When's the balloon going up, Postie?' asked Albie.

Instead of carrying his postbag, old Postie had more important things to do today. As his mates marched off, he was left behind to guard the makeshift entrance to the bandstand. 'LDV' it said on his armband.

'That means Local Defence Volunteers,' said Charlie, knowingly.

Postie stood with his tin hat firmly in place, gas mask across his shoulder, boots polished so that we could see our faces in them, and not to be forgotten were his Great War medals proudly fixed in place.

Left, right, left, right, Postie's mates marched off. Mr Golding nudged Harry Ponder and said, 'Scruffy-looking lot if you ask me.'

His friend nodded in agreement. 'Dunno what our sergeant would have made of 'em.'

Come on, we're going to see if they've finished the air raid shelters yet.'

'Oi, Postie,' Albie Gibbs called out. 'Do you want to borrow our Billy's pop gun?'

We all raced off across the park before Postie could reply!

'Please, sir, what does it mean, "Peace in our time"?'

We felt sure that Steppo had asked old Murray the question to delay the closing of our history books, before moving on to our arithmetic ones.

'Well, Stephens, it means, I hope, what it says: peace in our time.'

He went on to say that Mr Chamberlain had arrived back in London from Germany waving his scrap of paper signed by Herr Hitler to save us all from the horrors of another war. Given half a chance Mr Murray would always enlarge upon the fearful side of war. We all knew that he had been to France in the Great War.

Every so often during term time, Mr Lethaby, our headmaster, would come into the classroom and tell us, 'Mr Murray will not be at school for a few days. I want you all to behave yourselves. What lesson should you be doing now?'

'Geography, sir.'

'Well, take out your atlases and

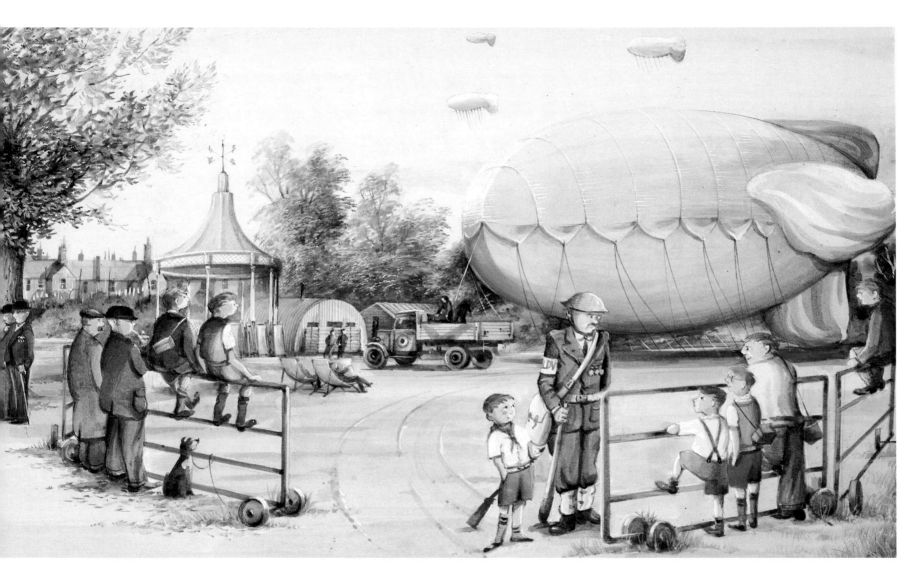

exercise books and get on with it, and I don't wish to hear any noise and no skylarking about. Understood?'

'Yes, sir,' we all chorused.

'He's got shellshock, like my old uncle,' said a voice from the back of the class. Often, when he was writing on the blackboard his hand would shake, making it difficult for him to finish the word he was endeavouring to write. We held our breath as he struggled to keep his hand steady. We willed him to do it, as to most of us he was very popular, especially on Saturday mornings when rain or shine he would organise our football games. Some days as he struggled there would be a snigger from the back of the class, whereupon he would turn round and hurl the piece of chalk in the direction from where he thought snigger had come.

Later, in the park, we asked Parky, 'Why are they still digging up our football pitches for air raid shelters, cos our teacher Mr Murray says there's not going to be another war. It's peace in our time, he told us.'

'Well,' said Parky, 'I don't know so much about that, cos I wouldn't trust that old Hitler further than I could throw 'im.'

The Sunday bike ride

'You've more patches than tube there, lad.'

'How much longer are you going to be, Podgy?' we called out every two or three minutes.

'Nearly finished,' he replied.

'Well, we 'aven't got all day,' we answered back, adding, 'We'll never get there,' and 'Why don't you get yourself a new inner tube?'

We never knew where 'there' was because on our bike rides we just set off, always in the same direction that took us first to Wanstead, on to Lambourne End and Abridge and down the High Street in Epping. From then on it was anybody's guess, as all the signposts had been taken down so that if old Hitler came he wouldn't know where he was going, just like us! Anyway, we never really cared – we never admired the views. Our aim was just to be on our bikes and in the green countryside.

When we had come back from the evacuation we were all suddenly 14, and went to see Mr Murray at Balaam Street for the last time and to collect our school report. Armed with this we had set off to find our first jobs. For the first time we were going our separate ways, but weekends found us together again.

The Free Ferry at Woolwich, the Flats and the park were no longer our playgrounds. With our grown-up bikes we wished to venture further afield. And Uncle Bill kept his promise to me of long ago and stopped my Sunday penny!

'Oh come on, Podgy, we'll never get there.'

Podgy's inner tube had been a cause of concern for many Sundays. Old Chambers, with his cat, had been watching Podgy's efforts for the last ten minutes or so. At long last Podgy stood back to admire his handiwork and yet another patch. Mr Chambers spoiled his moment of triumph when he said, 'You've more patch than tube there, lad. Mark my words, you'll not get far on that today.'

As we circled round and round to curb our impatience with Podgy and his puncture, the driver of an Austin Seven bipped his horn. Of course, cheeky Albie would have none of that.

'Oi,' he said, with one foot resting on the running board. 'Oi, is your journey really necessary, and don't you know there's a war on, mister?'

Mister's reply was audible to us all, and we hastily made way for mister and his wife to get on their way.

The barrage balloons were high in the sky, the spring sunshine turning them into fat, silver fish, as with a tinkling of bells and a wave to old Mr Chambers we pedalled off to enjoy the highways and byways of our newly found distant countryside.

Any old iron

'You ought to give that bit of old iron to the war effort!'

The big clock struck one o'clock over the High Street in Epping. Alf and myself led the way as we pedalled along. Turning to him I said, 'I know the way to Chipping Ongar from here.'

When Bobby was learning to drive, a distant elder cousin who was teaching him said occasionally, 'Let's have a ride out into the countryside today, Bobby, and see how you manage in the narrow lanes.' Being the back-seat passenger I soon recognised the familiar landmarks and came to know my way around.

'Right, Bobby,' George would say. 'Let the clutch in nice and smoothly, gently does it, foot on the accelerator. Look in the rear mirror now to see if anything's coming, and off you go.' With a jolt and a jerk Bobby would pull away from the curb.

'Bobby, I said smoothly and gently.'

With a sideways look Bobby would say, 'Sorry, George.'

'Don't look at me, look where you're going!' George would bellow. Poor old Bob's ears turned redder than ever.

'We can stop here,' I said, as we cycled off the roadway and into an open field. The others quickly followed behind. Scoffing our small snacks, it wasn't long before someone produced a tennis ball. The inevitably coats went down to form a makeshift goal and soon Ernie was diving around like his namesake Ernie Gregory down at West Ham. It was mid-afternoon when we pedalled off again.

'Oi!' Eddy shouted. 'Podgy's not here.'

We all stopped. 'Where is he?'

'I'll go back and see where he is.'

Five minutes later Eddy came back. 'Podgy's got another puncture.'

With moans and groans we all turned round and went back to him. Podgy, as ever, was standing over his now hated back wheel. His bike was upturned on the grassy, stony verge, and his now so familiar toolbag lay open on the ground beside him.

'Old man Chambers was right,' we all exclaimed. 'How long's it going to be to fix it?'

'Not long,' he said. 'I've got another patch.'

Over our heads roared a squadron of fighter planes. There was a brief argument.

'They're Hurricanes,' somebody said.

'Oh no they're not, clever Dick, they're Spits,' Charlie Mount said, adding, 'Hurricanes have got their wings clipped – those up there 'aven't.' Hurricanes or Spitfires, Heinkels or Messerschmitts, Podgy and his rotten old inner tube were the enemy that Sunday afternoon. We could do nothing but sit around and wait for him to get to work with another of his magic patches.

Sitting behind their sandbags outside their pillbox the local LDV sat in the sunshine, waiting for Jerry to come.

''ere!' one of them called out, 'you ought to give that bit of old iron to the war effort.'

That's what we all thought about Podgy and his bike at that moment! Two contented cows looked over the fence at us, as much as to say, 'Hello, hello, what's going on here then?'

'That's fixed it,' Podgy announced.

We helped him put the wheel back on, then got on our bikes, calling out as we did so, 'Oi you, you can go back to sleep now. Jerry's not coming today.'

With that we pedalled off as fast as we could. I bent low over my Hercules racer. I had saved up 25 shillings for it during the long winter months, and Mum had given me the extra 25 shillings. I was very proud when I handed over the 50 bob to the man in Bates's bike shop in the Barking Road and wheeled my racer home.

Tired out now, we pedalled down Balaam Street. The sun was beginning to go down. Alf turned to me and said, 'Call for you in the morning, Ken,' because we both set off for the city on the same tram. He travelled to Aldgate, and I went on to Clerkenwell. Not to school, but out to work with our long 'uns on – we were 14 and grown-up with it!

The Anderson

'Ken, look I've a jam-jar full of shrapnel already.'

'Ken, cor, look at this.' Bunny held up his latest shrapnel find for me to see. 'I've a jam-jar full already, and my Uncle Jack who works in the Woolwich Arsenal said he could make a cigarette lighter with all the bits I've collected.'

The 'all clear' had just sounded. The Chambers family climbed out of their Anderson and trooped indoors, not seeming to be concerned about Bunny's latest find. Mum opened the bedroom window.

'Ken,' she called. 'You'll be late for work, specially if the trams aren't running, like yesterday.'

Luckily they were, and shortly afterwards I was sitting on top of the No 65 on the way to Clerkenwell.

When I thought of the long, hot summer day when Bob and I helped the Chamberses to dig the hole! Next door's Anderson was a posh affair, with bunk beds, an oil stove, oil-cloth on the floor and a heavy curtain that covered the entrance. Fat, rosy red tomatoes and lettuces

covered the top. We didn't use ours much. Mum preferred to get under our big kitchen table or under the stairs when the raids were on. She said she didn't like all the creepy-crawlies and the musty old smell.

There was much excitement when the Anderson arrived, all shiny and bright as it was carefully stacked against the railings outside the parlour window. It was hot work and Mr Dixon in the corner shop did a roaring trade in lemonade powder to satisfy our thirsts. Old Mr Chambers, of course, told us all what to do and at long last the hole was dug – 3 feet deep, 7 feet long and 5 feet wide he insisted it had to be.

The big moment arrived when he carefully carried all the bits and pieces down the passage.

'Mind my wallpaper,' Mrs Chambers kept calling out. She opened the kitchen window, as the larger pieces wouldn't negotiate round the copper in the scullery. We carefully handed out each piece into the back yard through the open window, then gathered round the hole.

'No playing about, now,' Mr C. said as he endeavoured to make head or tail of the instructions that were in the big brown envelope that came with all the bits and pieces. Occasionally scratching his head, he at long last said, 'Ah, I've got it.'

He stood in the hole with Wally, his eldest son, while the rest of us handed down with great care the components as he asked for them.

'Nut and bolt,' he shouted. I was in charge of these and hastily handed down one of each into his outstretched hand. As he rolled his sleeves further up his arms, I became aware from the tattoo on his arm that old Chambers's first love was 'Gladys'.

'Spanner.' Bunny was in charge of the spanner.

After lots more nuts and bolts and more lemonade, the last bit was in place, secured with the last nut and bolt. It was getting dark as we hastily shovelled all the dirt back on top of the gleaming Anderson.

'What a shame to cover it all up,' said Bob.

Mrs Chambers appeared with a rolled-up Union Jack, a left-over from the coronation.

''ere,' she said. 'I know you'll be looking for this.'

Old Chambers hammered the shaft into the loose dirt. 'That'll show old Hitler what for.'

A week later we all assembled in our back yard. I said to Bob, 'I wonder if we'll find any buried treasure when we dig the hole.'

Mum, overhearing, said, 'You might find what's left of your gran's old cat.'

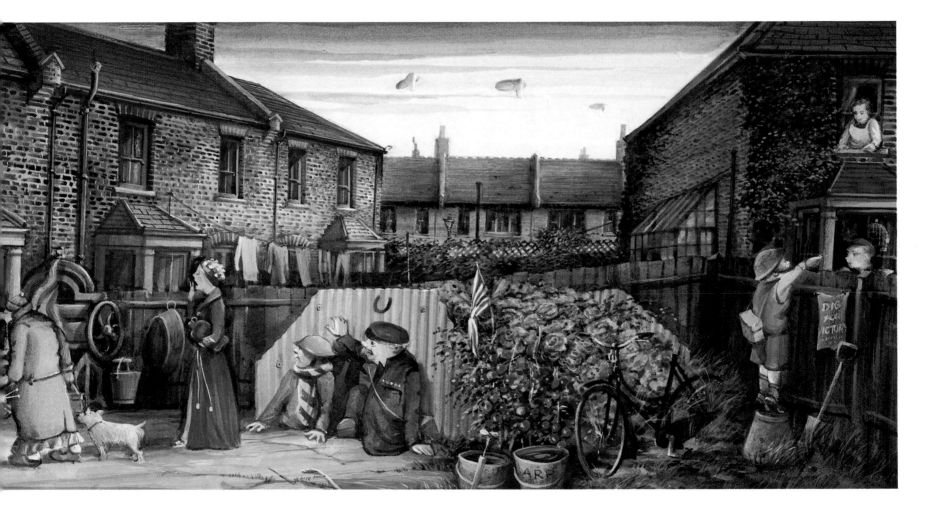

The long walk from Aldgate to Clerkenwell

'And where are you off to, Sonny Jim?' 'Clerkenwell Road,' I said.

'Where are you off to, young man?' asked the air raid warden.

'Clerkenwell Road,' I replied.

'You have to go through the churchyard this morning,' he said, indicating with his thumb. My look conveyed my thoughts, when he said, 'It's all right, Sonny Jim, there's nothing in there that'll bite you.'

I hurried through the entrance, endeavouring to catch up with those who had passed through a moment before.

I had walked from Aldgate. The conductor on the No 67 tram had said with a laugh, 'It's as far as we go this morning, cos there's bombs on the line further up the road.'

Leaving the churchyard, I turned into Old Street, crossed Goswell Road and walked down Clerkenwell Road. Nearly there, I thought. At last the pavements were free of debris and firemen's hoses. It all looked as it had on Friday, although the smell of burning wood, brick dust and oily water lingered on in my nose. Ah, there in the distance I could see the old Butler & Crispe sign, manufacturing and wholesale chemists since 1777. Still there, I thought. I hurried along – gosh, I

am going to be late this morning, although it must be afternoon now. Hope Mr Rodgers will understand that I had to walk a long way.

I turned into Albemarle Way and saw the vans being loaded for tomorrow's deliveries.

'Oi, Kim!' called out one of the drivers. 'Couldn't you get up this morning? And what happened to your team on Saturday? Couldn't play for toffee, that lot.'

'You wait till we play Fulham next Saturday,' I said.

I climbed the stone steps, reached up to the shiny brass handle and went up the stairs two at a time to the counting house.

'Hello, young Kimberley,' old Rodgers, the counting house

manager, said. 'We didn't expect to see you today. Plaistow, is it, where you live?'

'That's right, sir,' I replied. 'I had to walk from Aldgate.'

'Did you? Well done, lad, and now you pop in the kitchen, put the kettle on and we'll all have a cup of tea. Then I think you had better get off home before it gets dark. Oh, and before you go, pop across the road to old Harris and see if he's got my St Julian will you? He said he would save two ounces for me.' He stopped at the senior ledger clerk's desk and said to Mr Griffiths, 'Young Kimberley walked all the way from Aldgate, you know, Griff.'

As I put the kettle on I felt pleased with myself.

'The war's not so bad after all,' I thought, 'specially if we beat Fulham on Saturday!'

Firewatching

'I've brought you up a cup of tea in the Thermos, Mr Griffiths.'

'Mum, is it all right if I do firewatching tomorrow night?'

'Do what?' she asked. 'Where?'

'In the office up at Clerkenwell,' I replied.

'Oh, I don't know about that. Whose idea is this?'

'Well, it's not that I'll be doing any real firewatching, it's just that I'll be down in the basement making tea, while the men like Mr Griffiths go up on the roof and keep a look-out when there's a raid on.'

'How often will this be?' she asked.

'Oh, only about once a week, and I'll get paid three shillings a night,' I added enthusiastically.

She went into the scullery, saying, 'We'll see.'

'Will it be all right then, Mum?' I asked later that evening.

'Are the other boys doing it?' she asked.

'Oh yes,' I said. 'We'll be taking it in turns, all except one cos his father is a conscientious objector and won't let him.'

'You'll be in the basement all the time then.'

'Oh, of course, Mum,' I replied. There's sandbags down there and camp beds and it's all been strengthened with large bits of wood and iron posts. It's smashing, there's a wireless set, a ping-pong table and a shove-halfpenny board. It's ever so comfortable down there.'

'Oh, all right then,' she said, almost despairingly I thought. 'You'll have to take some extra sandwiches then.'

'Gee, thanks Mum.'

They were playing cards when the telephone rang. Mr Griffiths answered it.

'OK Bob, we'll be up,' he said.

'Oh blast,' said Ben Tollhurst. 'It's the best hand I've had all night.'

They quickly put their overalls, gumboots and helmets on and with their gasmasks across their shoulders they were all unrecognisable – I had never seen them before except in their dark office suits. As they went up the stairs, Mr Griffiths called back to me, 'Keep the kettle going, Kim.'

I carried the used cups and saucers across to the sink, washing and drying them, then laid them out neatly alongside the tea caddy and bottle of milk. I put the lid back on the biscuit tin, yawned and stretched; looking at my watch I saw that it was half past eleven. I took my wristwatch off and gave it a polish with my handkerchief. The time passed slowly by. I know, I'll make some tea. I'm sure they'd like a cup up on the roof. I could take them one up in the Thermos flask!

Five minutes later I climbed the stairs to the ground floor with the flask under my arm. Gosh, I

thought, I'd better put a helmet on. I hurried back down to the basement. Gee, it's a bit big, I thought, as it slipped over my ears. Never mind, Mr Griffiths can't tell me off now for not wearing one.

I passed all the boxes and packages lined up in the warehouse for the morning's deliveries, 'Town' on one side, 'Country' on the other, all neatly stacked with their delivery notes carefully attached. I felt the warmth from the vacuum flask under my arm as I went up the stairs to the first floor then the second, where our counting house was. I opened the door to the attic staircase. It was up there that all the old ledgers were stored. I knew my way because during the summer months we office boys went out on to the roof and had our sandwiches.

Holding the Thermos to my chest I grasped the worn wooden handrail and went up the rickety wooden steps to the skylight door. It was always stiff, so I gave it a push with my free hand. It flew open.

I was expecting it to be pitch black, not broad daylight! Mr Griffiths was pumping away as fast as he could on a stirrup pump. Ben Tollhurst was laying outstretched. In one hand he had a dustbin lid and in the other he was directing the hose into the heart of the brightness. Somebody I couldn't readily recognise was replacing the

empty buckets with full ones. Briefly my eyes went beyond the scene before me. Flames were leaping through the roof of the pub opposite. Men were scrambling

over the roof of the Westminster Bank. My helmet slipped further down over my eyes and ears. The vacuum flask suddenly seemed too hot to hold.

'Mr Griffiths, Mr Griffiths, I've brought you up a cup of tea in the Thermos.'

His glasses had almost slipped off his nose and I could see the sweat running of his forehead. 'For Christ's sake, Kim, we've no time for b— tea. Get back downstairs and stay there.' He said it with such vehemence that I lost my grip on the skylight door, and slid back down the attic stairs.

I still held the Thermos, but my helmet fell of my head and hung round my neck by the strap.

Goodbye E13

My model railway had gone for ever – so too had E13.

The double doors in the counting house flew open.

'Here he comes,' we all thought, as we kept our heads down over our ledgers.

Mr Gower strode down the passageway between the high desks, his waxed moustache almost as wide as his face. His bow tie matched his tartan waistcoat.

'Morning all,' he boomed, loud enough to frighten the pigeons off the windowsills. As always, the managing director made a beeline for Alice, putting his arm around her ample waist and saying, 'And how's my little Alice today?' This routine had been going on for as long as the senior ledger clerks could remember, 20 years or more perhaps.

Alice Pratt was a middle-aged spinster, and it was the highlight of her day. She beamed her queen bee smile to one and all, just to make sure that we hadn't missed the big moment of her morning. Only then did she turn her attention back to her immaculately kept ledger, with its Bank of England hand-written script on every leaf. It would, I am sure, have made old Len Murray back at Balaam Street green with envy, and would deservedly have got ten out of ten.

One morning I answered the phone.

'Is Alice there?' the voice enquired.

'It's for you, Alice,' I said innocently, without a moment's thought.

'Alice? Alice?' she said, looking down at me from her high stool. 'It's Miss Pratt to you, young man, and don't you ever forget it.'

I learned later, however, that if you scratched away at the hard veneer, Alice was a softy at heart, caring at home for her elderly parents, forever rattling one of her collecting boxes around the firm for yet another good cause, and spending hours making up parcels for the lads who had left the company for the forces.

Bob Kimberley

'Why don't you play football or cricket or whatever?' I would ask him.

'Cos I'm not good enough at it,' he would say.

If he did anything he had to be best, like on Sunday mornings in the swimming-pool down Balaam Street. Where I would hesitantly jump in at the 3-foot end, old Bob would make for the high-level diving board and dive in at the deep end! Like when at an early age he had collected all sorts of certificates for swimming and a cherished bronze medal for life-saving! He wouldn't devote any time to anything when he knew that he would come off second best. Like when he matriculated with just about the highest possible marks from Plaistow Secondary School. Like when, with his portfolio under his arm, he got his first job in a commercial art studio in North London. Like when he became the youngest applicant to apply for the relatively new driving test. Of course he passed first time!

I knew from a very early age that I could never keep up with him. I was never envious, but pleased and proud that my big brother was one of the brightest lads in East 13.

In our early days walking along the pier at Southend-on-Sea an aeroplane had flown overhead.

'I'd like to try that one day,' he had said.

Some years later his wish was granted when he came back from Canada with his RAF wings up. But he didn't want to fly around shooting this down or shooting that up. Like thousands of others in those war years he wanted nothing more than to get back to 'home sweet home'. 'There just ain't no place like it, kid,' he would write in his letters to me. He longed to get back to his young wife Christine, house and job.

But it wasn't to be. One evening in early September 1944 Bob came off second best off the Dutch coast, and his Fighter Bomber Squadron came home without him and his Beaufighter. Knowing old Bob I bet the odds were stacked against him!

That evening all those years ago I lost a loving brother and my best ever friend.

'Young man, I believe it's your mother on the phone. She would like a word with you.'

'Thank you, Miss Pratt.'

'Is that you, Ken?'

'Yes, Mum.'

'Listen carefully. On the way to work this morning I bumped into Mrs Alder. She said she's tired of

the bombing and Lil, her daughter, suggested she went and stayed with her for a time until things quietened down. She asked me if we would care to go with her for a break, as there's plenty of room in her house at Hornchurch. You might have to sleep on the floor, but it would be better than that old Anderson.'

'But Mum. . .'
'There's no buts about it. Do as I say. Go to Liverpool Street station when you leave work.' Do this, do that, she continued, ending by giving me the address to find in Hornchurch.
'Is Bob going?' I asked.
'No, he's staying at home.'

'So will I then.'
'Oh no you won't. Just do as I say and I'll see you this evening.'
I didn't fancy it at all, but I slept on the floor of a strange house in Hornchurch for the rest of the week.

'I'll call in and see how Bob is this evening.'

'Oh all right, but don't be late,' Mum said.
I got off the tram at the top feeling for the key in my pocket, so that if Bob wasn't in I could sit and wait for him. I knew that something was up when I saw the end of the street, the one I knew so well, covered in a dusty haze.

Shapes that were unrecognisable to me appeared and disappeared as the clouds of dust rose and settled. As I hurried along, the gutters became full of glass, the pavement scattered with slates and rubble. Out of it all, Bob came walking towards me, carrying a battered suitcase, his treasured portfolio tucked safely under his arm, his suit looking much the worse for wear, and there was old Paddy, on his lead walking beside him.

'What's up, Bob, what's up?'

'It's a mess, kid – no point in going back there,' he answered.

'But I want to see, I've got to see.'

'Oh all right then.'

We walked back together. People we had known all our young lives were carrying the remains of their furniture from their once proud and cared-for little homes. Firemen and ARP people in their overalls and gumboots, helmets and gasmasks over their shoulders were heaving debris aside. Old Dixon's shop blind was laying forlornly over the greater part of his shop that now lay spread out over the road. The old chewing-gum machine, still bright yellow, stuck up like a finger from the pile. Neat rows of little houses to left and right were now open to the sky.

'Sorry, lads, can't let you go any further.' The ARP man held up his gloved hand.

'But what about my model railway? I want to see if it's all right.'

'Not today you can't. Come back in a few days' time when we've sorted it all out.'

'Come on, kid, let's do as he says.'

'But what about my railway?' I insisted.

Bob became impatient. 'Oh you and your railway. What about my car?'

We never saw it again; it was garaged in the old stable next door to Mr Dixon's shop.

On the bus to Hornchurch, Paddy sat on Bob's lap. I looked dejectedly out of the bus window, deep down knowing that my railway had gone for ever and, for me, so had East 13.